GROWING POTATOES ORGANICALLY

from MARKET GARDEN *to* FIELD CROP

Bostock

A *COG* PRACTICAL SKILLS HANDBOOK

Canadian Organic Growers
Cultivons biologique Canada

Growing Potatoes Organically
from **market garden** *to* **field crop**
First published in 2008

Canadian Organic Growers Inc.
323 Chapel Street · Ottawa
Ontario · K1N 7Z2 · Canada
Tel.: 613-216-0741 Fax: 613-236-0743
www.cog.ca publications@cog.ca

Production
Editors:
Sheila Globus
Janet Wallace
Design and Layout:
Jean-Michel Komarnicki, JMK Image-ination
Cover design:
Lisandro Ponce
Cover photographs:
Laura Berman, GreenFuse Photos
Project Manager:
Kristine Swaren, Blue Chicory Communications

Library and Archives Canada Cataloguing in Publication

Bostock, Maureen, 1951–
Growing potatoes organically from market garden to field crop : a COG practical skills handbook / Maureen Bostock.
Includes bibliographical references.
ISBN 978-0-9808987-0-5
1. Potatoes.
2. Organic farming.
I. Canadian Organic Growers
II. Title
SB211.P8B67 2008 635'.2184
C2008-907702-4

Printed and bound in Canada

SINCE COG's inception in 1975, changes in the organic sector have been dramatic. A movement then struggling to be noticed is now a multi-million dollar industry with widespread consumer recognition and national standards backed by federal regulation.

Organic agriculture is now the fastest growing sector in agriculture, and as such it is the most economically and environmentally viable solution for Canada's rural areas.

COG plays a significant role by keeping organic agriculture in the public spotlight. Our policy and media work, educational materials, production statistics, scholarships, farmer training, market development, and the grassroots work of our fifteen regional chapters have a significant positive impact on organic growing in Canada.

Organic agriculture:

- helps Canada meet its Kyoto commitments by sequestering carbon in the soil and producing food with energy efficient methods
- increases soil organic matter and a diversity of living soil organisms
- improves water quality and quantity
- improves biodiversity
- improves the health of soil, plants, animals, farm workers, consumers
- increases farm financial viability by reducing dependence on inputs and providing farmers a fairer return for their products

COG IS A FEDERALLY REGISTERED CHARITY (no. 13014 0494 RR0001). Our members are farmers, gardeners, processors, retailers, researchers and consumers who share a vision of a sustainable bioregionally-based organic food system.

COG's MISSION is to lead local and national communities towards sustainable organic stewardship of land, food and fibre while respecting nature, upholding social justice and protecting natural resources.

JOIN CANADIAN ORGANIC GROWERS

OUR NATURE IS ORGANIC

Contents

Practical skills sponsorship

This handbook was funded in part by Agriculture and Agri-Food Canada through the Advancing Canadian Agriculture and Agri-Food (ACAAF) program. We wish to acknowledge the support of the following organizations for making this publication possible: the Investment Agriculture Foundation of British Columbia, the Manitoba Rural Adaptation Council, the New Brunswick Agriculture Council / Conseil Agricole Nouveau-Brunswick, the Territorial Farmers Association and the Yukon Agricultural Association.

Agriculture and Agri-Food Canada (AAFC) is pleased to participate in the publication of this guide. AAFC is committed to working with its industry partners to increase public awareness of the importance of the agriculture and agri-food industry to Canada. Opinions expressed in this handbook are those of Canadian Organic Growers (COG) and not necessarily AAFC's.

Agriculture and Agri-Food Canada   Agriculture et Agroalimentaire Canada

---

Financial assistance was received at the Series Partner level from:

The McLean Foundation

Financial assistance was received at the Supporter level from:

Willsie Equipment Sales Inc
www.willsie.com 800-561-3025

Acknowledgments

Maureen Bostock farmed in northwest British Columbia for ten years before moving to Sweet Meadow Farm in Balderson, Ontario with her partner, Elizabeth Snyder, in 2002. There she grows certified organic potatoes and a wide range of other vegetables. She is an organic inspector in the eastern Ontario region and is a member of the International Organic Inspectors Association. Maureen is a board member of the Ecological Farmers Association of Ontario and represents EFAO to the CGSB Organic Technical Committee which oversees amendments to the Canadian Organic Standards.

Susie Osler

Maureen Bostock (siting on the tractor) and Elizabeth Snyder

THIS HANDBOOK could not have been written without the insights and experience of the organic farmers featured in these pages. Thanks to Fred Dollar (Prince Edward Island), Marv Dyck (Manitoba), Henry Ellenberger (Ontario), Garrett Gillespie (Yukon), Don Kizlyk (Saskatchewan), Marcus Koenig (Ontario), Bruce Miller (British Columbia), Donald Roussy (Quebec), Isaiah Swidersky (Ontario), and Dan Vriend (Alberta).

Thanks to those who took the time to review and enhance the manuscript with their suggestions: Dr. Derek Lynch (Nova Scotia), Hugh Martin and Dr. Eugenia Banks (Ontario), and Bruce Miller (British Columbia); and to Bill Barkley who conducted one of the interviews in French.

Any errors or omissions are mine alone.

Maureen Bostock, November 2008.

1 Introduction

We think of organic farming as farming the way our grandparents did. While organic farming draws on many traditional farming practices, it also has been built upon modern research and experimentation to find new answers to old questions. Chemical agriculture evolved as a response to the overbearing pests and diseases that plagued farmers in the early twentieth century. The soil on many farms had become exhausted by intensive agriculture. Monoculture had become a common practice. Today, as a result of our understanding of soil management, organic farmers in Canada enjoy yields which approach the levels of our conventional colleagues. Organic farming has accomplished this using a method of production that feeds the soil and leaves a smaller ecological footprint.

"The management required for twenty acres of organic potatoes is about the same as five hundred acres of organic grain or two hundred acres of organic soybeans, and the value of the crop is about equal."
Marcus Koenig

Conventional potato farming employs a vast range of chemicals for fertility, weed, pest and disease control, top-kill, and prevention of sprouting in storage. Organic potato farmers have addressed most of these issues and eliminated the factors in potato production which contribute to chemical dependency. Crop rotation, organic inputs and strict cull pile sanitation have raised organic potato production to within 85 % of conventional yields in some regions.

Some challenges remain in producing a marketable crop: in parts of Canada, the climate is humid; in other regions, insect pests arrive with the hot winds from the south, for example. Strategies have been devised to minimize these environmental factors.

This Practical Skills handbook introduces organic potatoes as a valuable cash crop and provides an overview of organic potato production practices. Whether you are a conventional potato farmer, an organic farmer interested in potatoes as a new cash crop, or a farmer considering transition to organic production methods, this handbook can provide you with the practical skills to take to the field.

There are many reasons why farmers are considering a transition to organic farming. Most are concerned about the impact of pesticides and herbicides on the environment and on the health of the farm family. The link between human illness and pesticides has been well established. The cost of the health and environmental impacts of these chemicals to the taxpayer is estimated at $145-million annually in Ontario alone. [1]

The use of chemical inputs strains the ecosystem and has led to the decline of many bird, bat and insect species. This loss of biodiversity may increase our vulnerability to new pest challenges in the years to come.

The leaching of nutrients from conventional agricultural soils has resulted in nitrate poisoning of our rivers and lakes. This has affected shellfish in Prince Edward Island, produced pathogenic algal blooms in Ontario's inland lakes and resulted in high nitrate concentrations in forages in BC's Fraser Valley.

The onset of climate change has alerted us to the detrimental effects of industrial agriculture on the environment. With peak oil on the horizon, agricultural systems will no longer be able to rely on fertilizers made from increasingly scarce non-renewable resources.

Organic farming supports a healthy ecosystem and uses less energy to produce nutritious food. Lower input costs and higher prices for their products often lead to a greater net return for farmers. Farmers also benefit from a healthier work and living environment and healthier soils for all the crops in the rotation.

This Practical Skills handbook offers an overview of organic potato production methods, organic strategies for dealing with pests and diseases, crop rotation, fertility, and seed potato production. Detailed descriptions of potato pests and diseases, a complete listing of potato varieties and a discussion of soil science are beyond the scope of this text and are covered in the Chapter 1 Resource listing at the end of the book.

Footnotes

1 MacRae, Rod et al. 2006. *Ontario Goes Organic: How to Access Canada's Growing Billion Dollar Market For Organic Food.* World Wildlife Fund Canada & Organic Agriculture Centre of Canada.

2 Organic farming

Organic farming methods ensure the sustainability of the farm and the ecosystem. Organic farming is a stewardship in which the land and the environment are nurtured to optimum health. The principle of feeding the soil forms the foundation of organic agriculture and crop rotation is the cornerstone.

Tillage and cultivation practices used to grow potatoes can damage the soil structure and microorganisms, so maintaining soil health is particularly critical. Potatoes are a heavy feeder, requiring good soil fertility to produce a high yield of marketable tubers.

Inputs should be selected according to the principle that they neither harm the soil life nor the environment. Rather than use chemical fertilizers, organic farmers feed the soil microorganisms by building organic matter and using non-synthetic sources of fertility such as cover crops, composts and rock dusts.

Diverse habitat, such as wild lands and hedgerows, help provide a balanced environment in which birds, bats and beneficial insects can thrive. Chemical fertilizers, herbicides, pesticides and genetically engineered organisms are prohibited in organic agriculture.

By planting overwintering cover crops and leaving vulnerable slopes (those greater than 9%) in perennial forage, organic farmers protect their fields from erosion. The Canadian Organic Standards require organic farmers to develop a management plan to protect their soils.

The stewardship of organic farmers extends to ensuring that the potatoes retain their nutrition, vitality and organic integrity from the time of harvest until they reach the consumer or processing facility.

Organic certification

After June, 2009, products sold as organic for interprovincial and international trade will be required by federal regulation to meet the Canadian Organic Standards. The Consumer Packaging and Labelling Act is expected to enforce the use of the organic label in marketing within provinces.

Canadian Organic Standards

The Canadian Organic Standards consist of two parts:

1 CAN/CGSB – 32.310 Organic Production Systems – General Principles & Management Standards which defines the parameters of organic production as well as the requirements for handling and processing of organic foods; and

2 CAN/CGSB – 32.311 Organic Production Systems – Permitted Substances List which itemizes inputs that may be used on organic farms, including soil amendments, crop production aids, livestock materials, processing substances and sanitation materials.

The Canadian Organic Standards can be downloaded from the website of the Canadian General Standards Board at: www.pwgsc.gc.ca/cgsb/on_the_net/organic/index-e.html

The Canadian Organic Office of the Canadian Food Inspection Agency is responsible for enforcing the Canadian Organic Regulations. Regulatory information is available online at www.inspection.gc.ca/english/fssa/orgbio/orgbioe.shtml

Canadian Organic Growers answers frequently-asked questions and provides Standards information on its website www.cog.ca

Organic certification is required when marketing organic potatoes across provincial or national borders. To become certified organic, the land must pass through a transition period which is defined as thirty-six months from the date of the last application of non-permitted substances.

TRANSITION TO ORGANIC

The transition period serves three purposes:

- to clean the soil of prohibited substance residues
- to rebuild soil biology which has been disturbed by conventional inputs and practices
- to give the transitioning farmer time to absorb the lessons of a new approach to farming

The farmland must be under the purview of a certification agency for at least twelve months of the transition. An inspection is conducted during the final year of transition as well as once yearly thereafter.

If you have already been farming organically, you may be granted third year transition status, provided your fields can be shown to have been free of prohibited substances for the previous thirty-six months.

A farm management plan is required and must include field descriptions, buffers, source of inputs (including seeds, fertility amendments and crop production aids), pest and disease management strategies, as well as details on packaging, storage and transportation. Farm production records must be kept, including soil and source water test results and a journal of farm activities. Transport affidavits provide verification that organic products are kept separate from conventional products and free from contact with residues of prohibited substances.

Some farmers choose to put only selected fields through an organic transition rather than the whole farm. Making the transition one field at a time provides the opportunity to learn about organic farming and marketing gradually.

The farmer must ensure that the organic crop is separate from the conventional at all stages of production from growing, storing, transport and retail. Growing hay conventionally while growing potatoes organically, for example, poses few problems, except that the hay field requires a transition period if prohibited substances are applied, before it can come into organic production. Growing both organic and conventional potatoes may be permitted, but there must be obvious visible differences between them. The degree of separation must be significant enough to enable verification by the organic inspector. The crops would require separate fields and distinct storage. For example, a red-skinned variety could be grown organically if all of the conventional potatoes are white or yellow-skinned, given the visual differences between the varieties. Particular care must be taken by the farmer to ensure that conventional inputs are not applied to organic crops in error and that no commingling of organic and conventional potatoes occurs.

Poplar Grove Farm

Marv Dyck, southwest Manitoba

Cash crops:
alfalfa hay, field peas and oats, navy beans, vegetables and potatoes

Green manure:
alfalfa, peas, oats

Irrigation:
gravity-fed, 6–8 inches per year

Soil:
light sandy to sandy-loam, pH 8.0

Farm size:
567 hectares (1400 acres), with 100 hectares (250 ac) in potatoes

History:
certified organic by QAI since 2000

Spinosad is an aerobic fermentation product of Saccharopolyspora spinosa, soil bacteria which is used by organic farmers as a pesticide.

Marv Dyck is a member of the team which manages Poplar Grove Farm, the organic division of Kroeker Farms. Located southwest of Winnipeg, Manitoba, Poplar Grove Farm consists of 567 hectares (1400 ac), with 100 hectares (250 ac) in potatoes, 24 hectares (60 ac) in onions, and the remainder in field crops: alfalfa, peas/oats and navy beans. Preferred potato varieties include Norland, Chieftain, Viking and Yukon Gold.

Kroeker Farms also produce their own certified organic seed potatoes since the Manitoba Potato Seed Production Act requires that all potatoes grown for commercial production in the province come from a certified seed source. By producing their own seed, they reduce their costs significantly.

Colorado potato beetles (CPB) are the most troublesome pest at Poplar Grove Farm. Marv's control strategy is to perimeter spray with spinosad if the damage threshold becomes significant. This minimal control usually knocks CPB numbers back enough to prevent reduced yields.

"You have to walk the fields to know if it is time to take action," says Marv. "The most important principle of organic farming is to keep the crop vibrant. Use of a spinosad product is secondary." Marv noticed for example that the beetles seem to attack the weak plants. By not applying spinosad to the whole field, beneficial insects continue to work and nature is able to achieve a balance. To control leafhopper pressure and lower potato beetle infestation, Marv sprays diatomaceous earth mixed with sugar, which acts as a feeding irritant.

The fertility program includes applications of aged manure in the fall before the potato rotation: 22–69 metric tonnes per hectare (10–31 tons/ ac) is applied and incorporated immediately. At planting time, the crop's nutritional needs are supplemented with a side dressing of fish fertilizer.

Marv grows potatoes in rotation with two, three or four years of alfalfa and a green manure plow-down in the last year. When alfalfa is not used, he includes a green manure of field peas and oats in the rotation. Yields average 30 tonnes per hectare (13.5 tons/ac) and are 85% of local conventional yields.

3 Variety Selection & Potato Breeding

Variety selection

The Canadian Organic Standards require organic producers to use certified organic seed potatoes, unless they are not available commercially. To be granted an organic seed exemption, farmers are required to conduct a search of organic seed sources to ensure that the variety selected is not available as certified organic certified seed.

Organic potato farmers select varieties based on a number of factors including:

- response of the variety to local cultural conditions
- resistance to diseases
- market preferences
- niche market opportunities for unique varieties (e.g. French fingerlings or red skin/yellow fleshed Desiree)

Organic potato farmers may also choose varieties specifically suited to low-input organic production and local cultural conditions. Some varieties developed for conventional agriculture require high levels of nutrients to produce a marketable crop. Russet Burbank produces high yields when soil moisture and fertility are consistent throughout the growing season but is not well adapted to warmer regions of the country. Other varieties may be late maturing and require chitting or green sprouting to succeed in short-season locations. Still others may not perform well in a dry season.

A few of the varieties available for commercial production in Canada are featured in the following tables and were selected because they were preferred by the farmers interviewed for this book. When deciding on varieties to grow, consider your local growing conditions and market; it is not our intention to recommend these varieties above any others.

NOTES FOR THE TABLES:

MATURITY

Very early: 65 to 70 days days to maturity
Early: 70 to 90 days days to maturity
Midseason: 90 to 110 days days to maturity
Late: 110 to 130 days days to maturity
Very late: 130 days or more days to maturity

Where varieties note oversizing, hollow heart or chitting, see chapter 6 for production methods.

RED SKIN VARIETIES

VARIETY	MATURITY	COLOUR	USE	YIELD	CHARACTERISTICS
Chieftain	Early to midseason	Red skin, white flesh	Excellent for table potatoes	High; tubers may be small in drought	Round, moist, firm; good skin set, can be washed
Norland	Early	Red skin, white flesh	Popular new table potato	High	Oblong, moist & firm; susceptible to air pollution and moisture stress
Viking	Midseason, tubers size up early	Red skin, very white flesh	Table	High	Adaptable to adverse growing conditions; drought resistant; oversizing
Desiree	Midseason to late	Red skin, yellow flesh	Table	High	Rough tubers in heavy soil; resistant to hollow heart
Rote Erstling	Early	Rose-red skin, yellow flesh	Table	Medium to high	Heritage variety; round, medium dry; good storage

YELLOW FLESH VARIETIES

VARIETY	MATURITY	COLOUR	USE	YIELD	CHARACTERISTICS
Agria	Midseason to late	Light yellow skin; dark yellow flesh	Table	Very high	Long, large, oval tubers; dry, floury texture; excellent baking, boiling or frying; excellent storage variety
Cascade	Midseason	Buff flaky skin; cream coloured flesh	Processing & table	High	Oblong; hauled direct to processor from the field; poor storage
Estima	Midseason	Buff coloured smooth skin; light yellow flesh	Table & processing; good for cooking & frying	Very high	Oval; drought resistant ; oversizing
Hertha	Midseason to late	Smooth yellow skin; light yellow flesh	Table; very good for frying; good for boiling, baking or chipping	High	Good storage; dry texture; chitting
Penta	Midseason	White smooth skin	Table & processing; good for cooking; very good for frying	Medium to high	Round; medium dry texture; drought resistant
Sieglinde	Early to midseason	Smooth, white to yellow skin	Table; suitable for salads; not suitable for frying or chipping	Low to Medium	Medium to high drought resistance
Yukon Gold	Midseason	Yellow-buff skin	Table; good for boiling, baking & frying; not suitable for chipping	Low to medium	Dry, mealy texture; excellent storage variety; susceptible to air pollution

WHITE FLESH VARIETIES

Variety	Maturity	Colour	Use	Yield	Characteristics
Atlantic	Midseason	Lightly netted white skin	Processing for potato chips & frying. Table use: good for boiling & baking	High	Oval to round smooth; hauled direct to processor from the field; poor storage; oversizing and hollow heart
Eramosa	Very early	Smooth white skin	Early table; excellent for boiling & baking	High	Oval; good storage
Fianna	Midseason	Smooth cream skin	Processing for chipping; table	High	Oval; excellent storage
Goldrush	Midseason	Russetted skin, very white flesh	Table; excellent for boiling, baking and frying	High	Oblong; good storage; can be used for processing out of the field
Russet Norkotah	Early to midseason	Russetted skin	Baking; poor for boiling, chipping	Medium	Long to oblong; widely adapted; good storage
Kennebec	Midseason to late	Smooth, buff skin	Table; boiling, baking, chipping & frying	High	Elliptical to oblong; widely adapted; excellent storage; prone to greening; oversizing
Onaway	Early	Smooth white skin	Early table; not acceptable for processing	High	Round; drought resistant; oversizing
Superior	Early to midseason	Smooth buff skin	Table; fair to good for boiling, baking & frying; excellent for chipping	Medium	Oval to oblong; good storage; oversizing
Warba	Very early	Buff skin	Early table; good for boiling & baking, not good for chipping	High	Round
White Rose	Midseason	Smooth white skin	Table; good for boiling & baking, not good for chipping	High	Large, long elliptical; requires irrigation and consistent fertility; good storage

GOURMET VARIETIES

VARIETY	MATURITY	COLOUR	USE	YIELD	CHARACTERISTICS
Fingerling Salad	Late	Buff yellow skin, light yellow flesh	Table, waxy texture for salads	High	Subject to greening; good storage
French Fingerling (also known as La Ratte)	Midseason to late	Red skin, yellow flesh	Table, waxy texture for salads	High	Large size compared to Russian Banana; good storage
Russian Banana	Late	Buff yellow skin, light yellow flesh	Table; waxy texture for salads	High	Large production of small tubers
All Blue (also known as Russian Blue)	Midseason	Smooth, blue to purple skin, purple flesh	Table; moist flesh	Medium	Oblong, medium size tubers, grainy flesh

Derek Lynch

Variety Trials at Springwillow Farm, Cavendish, P.E.I

NEW VARIETY DEVELOPMENT

Marcus Koenig, who grows organic potatoes in Grand Bend, Ontario, points out that European varieties have been developed to adapt to a wide range of growing conditions and can perform well in a low-input organic system. They also possess better disease resistance than North American varieties that have been developed to produce high yields under optimum fertility and consistent moisture levels. Moreover, European breeding programs are designed to respond to consumer taste; in Europe, people buy potatoes according to the variety that suits a particular use and they enjoy a broad diversity of potato varieties in the marketplace.

It can take up to twelve years to develop a variety that can reliably breed true. Breeders select parent plants with the desired traits from the gene pool of either domestic or wild potatoes. They obtain pollen from the male plant and fertilize the ovule of the female plant by hand. Ovules develop into true seed balls. The seed balls are allowed to grow to maturity. After a couple of months, the seeds are squeezed out and dried, to be planted in the greenhouse.

Unlike the potato tuber which is a clone of its parent stock, each individual seed from a single seed ball produces marble-size tubers bearing characteristics quite different from either the parents or siblings. Some may be red-skinned, while others may be white, elongated or round.

The mini-tubers are planted in field trials. Tubers are discarded if they mature late, have rough or split skins, adhere strongly to the roots or show signs of virus, bacterial or fungal infections. Ten to fifteen percent of the mini-tubers are selected and planted out in further field trials until a new variety, which has demonstrated commercial potential, is selected.

INSECT RESISTANCE

Dr. Zenaida N. Ganga, a Canadian potato breeder, and Dr. Peter VanderZaag of SunRISE Produce of Alliston, Ontario, have been working together to develop new potato varieties. They are selecting for durable resistance to both pests and scab (*Streptomyces* spp). They hope to release a new variety by 2013 which crosses wild potato genetics with modern commercial varieties. [1]

Wild potatoes bear the gene for bitter leaves, containing high foliar glycoalkaloid, which discourages leaf eating pests such as the Colorado Potato Beetle. Their hairy leaves also possess glandular trichomes or hairs which rupture upon contact with insects such as leafhoppers, releasing a sticky substance that traps the larvae and discourages the adults from eating.

LATE BLIGHT RESISTANCE

Island Sunshine, developed by Gerrit and Evert Loo of Prince Edward Island, was selected from varietal crosses that survived pest and disease pressure in organic potato trial plots. Released in 1997, Island Sunshine is known for its high resistance to late blight and its unique ability to retain resistance, unlike other varieties whose resistance tends to diminish over time. Island Sunshine is a cross between two Dutch heirloom varieties (Red Irene and Alpha) and is a very late maturing variety (135 days) with round tubers, rough yellow skin and dark yellow flesh. The texture of Island Sunshine compares well with Yukon Gold but is moister. The potatoes hold their shape well when boiled. Chitting can help Island Sunshine adapt to a wider range of Canadian growing conditions.

Breeding for horizontal resistance can be practiced on the farm. Selecting parent stock that survived exposure to a variety of diseases in the field can pass a high degree of genetic resistance on to offspring. On-farm breeding programs can select for preferred traits such as early maturity, disease resistance, or yield, and so contribute to a broadening of the genetic diversity of potatoes.[2]

Dr. Carlo Leifert of Newcastle University in England believes that the only long-term solution to controlling late blight is an internationally coordinated breeding program that would preserve resistance in specific varieties by continuously backcrossing them with their parent stock. In addition to Island Sunshine, other potato varieties show significant late blight resistance and would be good candidates for such a program; these include Sarpo, Sante, Lady Balfour and Eva Balfour.

HERITAGE VARIETIES

"Recommercializing heritage potato varieties is a key element in preserving biodiversity."
Garrett Pittinger

With a personal collection of nearly fifty varieties, Garrett Pittinger is a leading advocate for heritage potatoes. Among the varieties that Garrett and other members of Seeds of Diversity Canada preserve are Ailes Roses, Bauer Grun's Rote Auge, Bintje, Corne du Mouton, Crotte d'Ours, Elmer's Blue, Kifelcer, Matsuyama, Mrs. Moehrle's Yellow Flesh, Papa Negra, and Siberian.[3]

On his farm near Pontypool, Ontario, Garrett practices field sanitation, roguing out plants that show signs of disease, yellowing or stunting. As a result, his yields of heritage potatoes have remained consistently high. He recommends that growers select tubers from the most productive plants.

Jean-Michel Komarnicki

A selection of potato varieties grown by Garrett Pittenger

Over one hundred varieties of heritage potatoes are maintained at the Potato Research Centre in Fredericton, New Brunswick, a program of Agriculture and Agri-Food Canada. Several heritage varieties at the Research Centre have been cleaned of viruses, and samples are available to growers upon request (see Chapter 3 Resources at the end of the book).

GENETIC ENGINEERING

Organic farmers are concerned that the release of genetically engineered crops containing *Bacillus thuringiensis* var. *tenebrionis* (BTT) will reduce its effectiveness, as it is one of only a few bacterial agents allowed in organic agriculture. Colorado potato beetle resistance to pesticides has been found to occur within four to ten generations of repeated spraying.[4] When the beetle larvae eat the genetically modified potato plants, they are exposed to BTT in every cell of the leaves. Consequently, resistance is likely to develop more quickly, compared to when BTT is sprayed or used as a last resort, as in organic agriculture.

Genetically modified potato varieties containing BTT genes to repel the Colorado potato beetle were released in 1995 under the names of New Leaf, New Leaf Y and New Leaf Plus. The altered Russet Burbank and Shepody varieties performed very poorly in field tests and never achieved more than 3% of the total conventional potato crop in the U.S. In 2001, these varieties were discontinued and they are no longer registered for use in Canada.

Since potatoes are the fourth largest crop in the world[5], a successful genetically engineered potato could be profitable for the biotechnology industry. In 2008, an application was made in England to permit the commercial release of a variety genetically engineered for resistance to potato cyst nematodes. The potato contains a chemical which kills the nematodes in the root zone around the potato. Concerns have been raised that beneficial nematodes will be indiscriminately killed along with the potato cyst nematodes.

Syngenta has been field testing 'terminator technology' in England and Peru with the goal of developing a potato that will not sprout in storage. Terminator technology would be used to render the tubers sterile until a chemical is applied to stimulate sprouting. Unfortunately, conventional producers may welcome this technology as an improvement over the use of Chlorpropham which prevents potatoes from sprouting in storage.

Many South American farmers fear that Terminator genes will escape and spread sterility to wild and traditionally cultivated potato species in the Andes. As potatoes reproduce by tubers, genetic transfer from one variety to another would seem difficult, yet potatoes are able to hybridize naturally in the wild. The threat of Terminator technology spreading to other potatoes should not be underestimated.

FOOTNOTES

1 Ganga, Z. N. & VanderZaag, P. 2007. Breeding and Selection for potato varieties that are insect resistant, utilizing trichome-mediated host plant resistance; and have durable resistance to common scab (*Streptomyces spp.*). Project 8928 Final Report. Unpublished.

2 Robinson, Raoul A. *Amateur Potato Breeders Manual.* Free download from www.sharebooks.ca

3 Duclos, R. & Iarocci, A. The Potato Speaks For Itself. *Seeds of Diversity Journal,* vol.20 no.3, www.seeds.ca

4 Ragsdale, D. & Radcliffe, E. 2007. *Colorado Potato Beetle.* Dept. Of Entomology, University of Minnesota. www.vegedge.umn.edu/vegpest/cpb.htm

5 Food and Agriculture Organization (FAO) of the United Nations Year of the Potato, 2008. www.potato2008.org

Across the Creek Organics

Bruce and Brenda Miller, Pemberton, BC

Cash crops:
hay, vegetables and potatoes

Livestock:
cow/calf

Green manure:
red clover, oats

Irrigation:
gravity-fed sprinkler

Soil:
silt loam floodplain, pH 5.1–5.5

Farm size:
200 ha (500 acres), 18 ha (45 ac) in potatoes

History:
certified organic by PACS since 1999

Bruce and Brenda Miller farm on the banks of the Lillooet River, 160 kilometres north of Vancouver, on a farm that has been in their family since 1912. Surrounded by 2591 metre (8,500 ft) mountains in the Coastal mountain range, the 200 hectare (500 acre) farm consists of 100 hectare (250 ac) of fertile land with a bioreserve of wetlands and old growth cedar groves. The climate offers significant rainfall and is moderated by Interior weather patterns which are dry and hot in the summer. The soil is silt loam floodplain.

The Millers grow certified organic potatoes on 18 hectares (45 ac) and sell them either as certified organic certified seed or table stock. With yields of 22.4 tonnes per hectare (10 tons/ac), the Millers market their table stock potatoes to restaurants, grocery stores and several wholesalers. They sell seed potatoes to customers who find them through the Coalition of Organic Associations of British Columbia website – www.certifiedorganic.bc.ca. Among the varieties they grow are Yukon Gold, Sieglinde, Desiree, Chieftain, White Rose, Cascade, Russian Banana Fingerlings and Russian Blue.

Potatoes are planted in May and harvested in September. Getting the crop planted on time is important so the plants can mature and tubers can be harvested before the wet coastal fall weather.

The Pemberton Valley is protected by the British Columbia Seed Potato Control Act which requires that any seed brought into the valley is tissue culture that has been certified to be free of viral and bacterial organisms. Because of this stringent control the Pemberton Valley remains free from infection by mosaic viruses which are a major problem in other parts of the province. The disadvantage is that three years of planning are required to introduce new varieties.

The Millers had been conventional potato producers, but found the risk and low price threshold unacceptable. They decided to transition to organic production beginning with a few acres. Encouraged by the yield and quality, they increased their organic acreage each year, while watching the organic market continue to grow and match their production. For a number of years, they supplied a 100-member CSA with fresh organic vegetables to fill the gap in their income.

The Millers rotate their fields with four years of legume-rich forages and one year in potatoes. Fields coming out of forage into potato production are rotovated in the fall, followed by chisel plowing in both directions the next spring.

They use their own cow manure as a soil amendment but because they don't have enough, they have recently begun adding granular fish fertilizer at a rate of 336 kg/ha (300 lb / ac) at seeding.

Planting is done with a 2-row cup planter. Once the plants are about 8 cm (3 in.) tall with stocky stems, the Millers cultivate with a 3-point hitch tickle-weeder which is shaped to cover the hill.

They follow cultivation with hilling, using a plow-shaped two-row hiller. Cultivation and hilling are repeated three times during the season. Their most challenging weeds include shepherds purse, plantain, yellow dock and quackgrass.

When rainfall is insufficient, the Millers use an irrigation system that is gravity fed from a mountain stream 90 metres (300 ft.) above the valley floor and applied through overhead sprayers. They begin monitoring soil moisture on the 20th of June and provide no more than 2.5 cm (1 in.) of water per week if needed.

The Millers' most important defence against late blight is timely and complete top-kill with a vine beater. This also prevents viral diseases that may be carried by the large number of aphids that arrive in late summer. Top-kill matures the potato skin, protecting the tubers from injury in storage.

Green peach aphids can be a significant vector of potato diseases in the region. The Millers rely on a large population of native ladybugs which consume aphids voraciously.

The potatoes are harvested with a Grimme harvester which handles the potatoes very gently, preventing bruises which can cause disease in storage. The 648 square metres (7200 sq ft) storage facility can store 540 tonnes (600 tons) of potatoes. Air circulation operates 2–3 hours per day and provides a high volume of air exchange with a low velocity. The automatic system keeps the storage facility at a constant temperature of 4°C (38°F) over the winter.

Bruce notes that there is plenty of room for new producers in British Columbia to develop local niche markets for unique potato varieties with different flavours, colours and textures for consumers to enjoy.

Bruce Miller says: "If you can educate the consumer on flavour, you can develop a niche market."

4 Soil fertility on the organic potato farm

Soil fertility

The soil is a complex ecosystem. Our goal as organic farmers is to build a nutrient-rich and dynamic environment, in which the soil microorganisms can work to feed the plants. Some fundamental principles make this possible:

- keeping the soil covered year-round to retain nutrients
- using compost and cover crops to provide nutrients in a form that is easily taken up by plants
- supplying organic matter to support soil microorganisms which protect plants from soil borne disease
- rotating potato crops with three or four years of forage to allow time for the soil to recover from the impact of tillage

Potatoes prefer a sandy to sandy-loam soil with a pH between 5.5 and 6.0. They can, however, do well on heavy clay soils provided the seed potatoes are not planted until the soil has warmed up in the spring. Scab, which detracts from the potato's appearance, can be a problem in soils with a pH higher than 6.0. Potato varieties that are resistant to the scab organism include Superior, Cherokee, Onaway, Norland and Pike. [1]

Fertility requirements

Potatoes are heavy feeders and require significant amounts of nitrogen, phosphorus and potassium to produce a high yield of marketable tubers. Potatoes also benefit from trace nutrients supplied by applications of composted manure in the previous season.

A crop of new potatoes removes a total of 70 kg/ha (62 lb/ac) of nitrogen and just over a third of the total phosphorus, potassium and sulphur that would be taken up by a full season crop of potatoes.

CWTs are "hundred weights", each weighing one hundred pounds.

The chart below[2] describes the nutrients removed by a crop of potatoes yielding 33.6 tonnes/hectare (15 tons or 300 cwt/ac)

NUTRIENTS REMOVED BY POTATOES

PLANT PART	NITROGEN N	PHOSPHATE P_2O_5	POTASH K_2O	SULPHUR S
Tubers	107 kg/ha 96 *lb/ac*	31 kg/ha 28 *lb/ac*	181 kg/ha 162 *lb/ac*	10 kg/ha 9 *lb/ac*
Vines	84 kg/ha 75 *lb/ac*	25 kg/ha 22 *lb/ac*	69 kg/ha 62 *lb/ac*	6 kg/ha 5 *lb/ac*
Total	191 kg/ha 171 *lb/ac*	56 kg/ha 50 *lb/ac*	250 kg/ha 224 *lb/ac*	16 kg/ha 14 *lb/ac*

CROP ROTATION

Crop rotations should be planned to provide the nutrients required by the potato crop, and to rejuvenate the field in the years following potatoes. By growing alternate crops, the soil can rebuild its nutrient reserves and the cycle of pests and diseases can be broken. It also gives the soil a break from the compaction caused by heavy equipment used in potato farming. Research by Dr. Derek Lynch[3] and Dr. Gilles Boiteau on commercial organic farms in Atlantic Canada shows that extended rotations of 4–5 years help populations of soil organisms (bacteria, fungi and earthworms) re-establish from the disturbance of cultivation, hilling and harvesting.

Mycorrhizal fungi are one group of microorganisms that is disturbed by the tillage activities of row cropping. Cultivation cuts fungi hyphae, thereby reducing the nutrient exchange with plants. Compaction also reduces oxygen in the soil, which is needed by plants and beneficial microorganisms.

See Chapter 8 for more information on wireworms

Forage plowdown is the most common way that organic farmers supply nutrients to the potato crop. Unfortunately, when permanent pasture is plowed down, wireworms and white grubs can become serious pests in the subsequent two years.

Alfalfa and other legumes can be grown for hay and then incorporated as a green manure. A good stand of alfalfa can provide 288 kg N/ha (267 lb/ac) when inoculated with rhizobia and provided with adequate soil moisture.[4]

If, however, alfalfa is harvested as a forage crop and exported off the farm, potassium losses can be significant. Applications of composted manure can restore potassium levels required for high yields of potatoes, as well as supply additional nitrogen, phosphorus and micronutrients.

Forage plowdown generally consists of a grass/legume combination. The table below describes the nitrogen available to the succeeding crop depending upon the percentage of legume in the forage plowdown. A forage plowdown with less than 50 % legume will not provide sufficient nitrogen to the potato crop and require supplementation.

AVAILABLE NITROGEN FROM THE FORAGE PLOWDOWN[5]

RATIO OF LEGUME TO GRASS IN FORAGE PLOWDOWN	NITROGEN SUPPLIED
Less than ⅓ legume	ZERO
⅓ to ½ legume	55 kg/ha (49 *lb/ac*)
½ or more legume	110 kg/ha (98 *lb/ac*)
Perennial legumes seeded & plowed in the same year, where the stand is thick and over 40 cm (16 in) high	80 kg/ha (71 *lb/ac*)
Soybean & field bean residue	30 kg/ha (26 *lb/ac*)

Preliminary research into the timing of forage tillage reveals some interesting trends.[6] Fall plowing results in a marked reduction in available nitrogen (20–30 kg N/ha) to the following crop when compared with spring plowing. Fall plowing is a traditional approach which opens up the soil and exposes weeds to the winter freezing and thawing cycles; this kills annual and some perennial weeds. Organic farms that rely on the carryover of nitrogen from the incorporation of forages should weigh the benefits of fall tillage against the loss of 38 % of available nitrogen. An alternative is to plant a fall catch crop after tilling to take up some of the nitrogen that might otherwise leach away.

Potatoes fit well in rotation with leguminous hay and small grains, and can be included in a five-year grain rotation[7].

Five-year grain rotation

Year One	Cereal underseeded with legume
Year Two	Legume cover crop
Year Three	**Potatoes** followed by fall rye
Year Four	Fall rye harvested followed by a cover crop
Year Five	Soybeans

Vegetable growers work with crop rotations that alternate different families of vegetables. Eliot Coleman[8] recommends an 8-year rotation.

Vegetable growers should also incorporate forages in their rotations periodically as alternating the crop type can be an effective weed control strategy.

Eight-year vegetable rotation

Year One	Corn
Year Two	**Potatoes**
Year Three	Squash underseeded with sweetclover
Year Four	Root crops
Year Five	Beans
Year Six	Tomatoes underseeded with red clover
Year Seven	Peas followed by cover crop
Year Eight	Cabbage

Organic inputs

The Canadian Organic Standards require crop rotation and the incorporation of organic plant and/or animal matter to be the primary sources of soil fertility, thereby recycling nutrients on the organic farm. Other sources of nutrients, either off-farm or conventional, are viewed as supplemental. Consult the Permitted Substances List for allowed inputs and details regarding their use.

The Canadian Organic Standards prohibit the application of synthetic fertilizers, sewage sludge, genetically engineered organisms and substances which contain heavy metals. For more information on soil amendments, see the resource list at the end of the book.

GREEN MANURES

Using legumes as cover crop in rotation with potatoes is the most efficient way for organic farmers to supplement nitrogen,[9] as legumes fix atmospheric nitrogen through their symbiotic relationship with rhizobium bacteria.

Although rhizobia are often present in the soil, the rate of nitrogen-fixation can be enhanced by using a commercial inoculant which increases the nodulation on each plant. Successful cover cropping depends upon selecting a legume that is adapted to local soil and environmental conditions, and seeding at a time when good soil moisture ensures fast germination.

When included in the rotation, green manures provide a short-term return by supplying nitrogen and building organic matter to support the following potato crop. Green manures also contribute towards long term health of the soil as they:

- reduce nutrient leaching
- take up nutrients that would otherwise leach out
- make nutrients available to plants upon decomposition
- harvest nutrients from the subsoil
- break up hardpans
- build humus
- prevent erosion caused by rain or wind
- improve the soil's water retention
- increase biological activity
- outcompete weeds
- suppress weeds through an allelopathic effect
- prevent pest build-up by altering habitat
- provide habitat for beneficial insects
- suppress nematodes

Other factors to consider when selecting a legume include the price of seed and whether your forage is used for grazing or hay production.

Legumes can be overseeded into grain crops. While the legume fixes nitrogen, the grain produces biomass and fine fibrous roots which build organic matter in the soil. Grains which tiller, such as barley and rye, offer the added benefit of good ground cover that can choke out weeds. Some common cover crop combinations are barley/red clover, fall rye/red clover and oats/field peas.

GREEN MANURES

LEGUME	NITROGEN	DRY MATTER
Red clover	78–168 kg N/ha 70–150 *lb N/ac*	4.4–6.7 tonnes/ha 2–3 *tons/ac*
Field peas	100–168 kg N/ha 90–150 *lb N/ac*	4.4–5.6 tonnes/ha 2–2.5 *tons/ac*
Hairy vetch	100–224 kg N/ha 90–200 *lb N/ac*	2.5–5.6 tonnes/ha 1.2–2.5 *tons/ac*
Alfalfa	299 kg N/ha 267 *lb N/ac*	6.2–8.9 tonnes/ha 2.8–4 *tons/ac*
Sweetclover (yellow or white)	100–190 kg N/ha 90–170 *lb N/ac*	3.4–5 tonnes/ha 1.5–2.5 *tons/ac*

"Potatoes need to be placed in the rotation following small grains which create mellow soil."
Marcus Koenig

Check your provincial potato production manual to find out if Rhizoctonia solani is a problem in your region.

Potatoes benefit from a winter cover crop of fall rye planted the previous September. Rye has an allelopathic effect; both living and decomposing rye releases chemicals that suppress the germination of weed seeds. Rye also takes up nitrogen left over from the previous season and makes it available to the potatoes. Rye grows quickly in the fall and can germinate at temperatures as low as 1°C (34°F).

Buckwheat competes well with weeds and can develop a smothering canopy within five weeks. It also takes up phosphorus which is released to the following crop as the buckwheat residue breaks down. Buckwheat is a host for *Rhizoctonia solani* and may not be the best choice to precede potatoes in the rotation if Rhizoctonia is a problem in your region. [10]

Tap-rooted green manures such as sweetclover and alfalfa are very effective at breaking up hardpan. Alfalfa's taproots extend an average of three metres (ten ft.) into the subsoil. Yellow sweetclover is a biennial and requires two seasons to achieve its maximum potential. Sweetclover's main roots extend 0.3 metres (1 foot) into the ground and the side roots go down as much as 1.5 metres (5 feet). Although sweetclover can be grazed and cut for hay, mouldy sweetclover hay contains coumarin, a blood thinner that can be deadly to livestock.

COMPOST

Composted manure is an excellent resource, rich in nutrients for the soil and the potato crop. The composition of compost varies depending on the feedstock (materials used to make the compost). On average, one metric tonne (1.1 ton) of mature compost (composed of animal manure, urine and bedding properly composted) contains 20 kg (44 lb) nitrogen (N), 10 kg (22 lb) of phosphorus (P_2O_2) and 10 kg (22 lb) of potash (K_2O)[11] as well as trace minerals, living bacteria and organic matter.

Compost can be a cost-effective way to provide nutrients to the potato crop, particularly if livestock are part of the organic farm operation. Compost feedstocks may include animal manures, bedding, crop residue and household vegetable waste. These materials are combined in such a way that carbon and nitrogen are balanced at an ideal ratio between 25:1 and 35:1 before composting. At this ratio, enough carbon is present to feed aerobic microorganisms which capture nitrogen and transform it into a stable nutrient.

When compost is applied, thirty percent of the nutrients it contains are available to crops in the first year, with the remainder held over for another year or two. Applications of compost should not exceed the needs of the crop. If large amounts of compost are applied to a field year after year, potassium and phosphorus levels may become excessive in proportion to calcium and magnesium. Using a diverse crop rotation, growing green manures, and applying calcium can offset imbalances.[12]

Generally, compost is applied to the crop that precedes potatoes in the rotation or before planting a winter cover crop such as fall rye. When compost is applied more than 120 days prior to the potato harvest, it is not required to pass through a thermophilic phase (heating phase of 55°C / 131°F) as defined by the Canadian Organic Standards.

It is better to apply compost to a living cover crop than to apply it on bare ground. The cover crop takes up nutrients from the compost. When the cover crop is plowed under, the nutrients become available in a balanced ratio and in a form that the potato plants are able to utilize. When applied to bare ground, it is important to incorporate it into the soil as soon as possible to avoid the loss of nutrients.

The Canadian Organic Standards prohibit the application of raw manure or compost on frozen or snow-covered ground, or during the rainy season. Not only can the nutrient loss be excessive but the leaching of nutrients can pollute rivers and lakes.

PLANT AND FISH MEALS

Plant and fish meals: Formulations with permitted substances may also contain inert substances which are not listed on the Permitted Substances List of the Canadian Organic Standards. Check with your certifier to ensure that the product you wish to use is accepted under the standard.

Organic plant meals such as alfalfa or soybean meal, fish meal and fish foliar sprays are allowed as sources of nitrogen, phosphorus and micronutrients on organic farms. Alfalfa meal contains 5% nitrogen, 1% phosphorus and 2% potash as well as trace minerals and triaconatol, a growth stimulant. Soybean meal, a by-product of oil extraction, is more expensive but contains more nitrogen.

Fish meal contains 5% nitrogen, 3% phosphorus and 1% potash. Fish fertilizers that contain a minimum of 15% oil also support the growth of mycorrhizal fungi.

Foliar feeds do not improve soil health and should not be relied upon as the primary source of nutrients on an organic farm. As an efficient and quick boost in crop growth, fish emulsion can be used as a foliar spray to provide 4% nitrogen, 4% phosphorus and 1% potash.

ROCK DUSTS

Rock dusts include limestone, rock phosphate and other mined substances that can provide minerals needed for crop production.

- Calcitic lime (calcium carbonate) from seabed deposits is a good source of calcium and can be used to increase the pH of the soil. Soil tests can indicate whether the use of calcium carbonate will cause too much of an increase in pH, which may increase the risk of scab.
- Dolomitic limestone supplies calcium and magnesium. It can be used to supply calcium and increase the pH instead of calcitic lime if levels of magnesium are low.
- Gypsum is a naturally occurring form of calcium sulphate, and does not increase pH. Gypsum contains 18% sulphur.
- Rock phosphates generally provide 1–2% of their total phosphate as available. Colloidal phosphate, which is composed of clay particles and phosphate ions, is often considered to be the best source of phosphate, but it is more expensive than other rock dusts.
- Sul-Po-Mag (langbeinite) is a magnesium-bearing potassium sulphate, which contains 11% magnesium and 22% potassium.
- Granite dust contains 4% total potassium, 67% silica and 19 micronutrients.
- Greensand is a seabed deposit with 7% potassium which is released very slowly to the crop. Greensand also contains iron, magnesium, silica and trace minerals.

KELP

Kelp meal is dried seaweed which contains 1% nitrogen, a trace amount of phosphorus and 2% potash, as well as magnesium, sulphur, trace elements and plant hormones. Soil application rates of 168 kg/ha (150 lb/ac) are used on forage and small grain crops, while horticultural crops and corn benefit from 446 kg/ha (400 lb/ac).

MYCORRHIZAL FUNGI

Mycorrhizal fungi are soil microorganisms which form symbiotic relationships with plants, enhancing their nutrient uptake and improving their disease resistance. When applied as a commercial inoculant, mycorrhizal fungi can increase yields significantly, boosting mycorrhizal activity in soil that has been disturbed by field preparation and cultivation.[13] Seed potatoes can be inoculated with mycorrhizal fungal spores at planting.

HUMATES

Leonardite is a naturally occurring oxidized form of lignite coal, derived from ancient peat bogs. Leonardite contains 85% humic acids which promote plant growth when applied at a rate of 336–560 kg/ha (300–500 lb/ac). Natural deposits of leonardite contain varying levels of heavy metals, a serious concern if applied in large volume to field crops. Ask the distributor about the percentage of heavy metal contamination and monitor levels to avoid a build up of heavy metals in the soil.

MOLASSES

Organic molasses or sugars are high carbon substances which provide food for microorganisms and stimulate biological activity in the root zone.

Footnotes

1 OMAFRA. *Vegetable Production Recommendations* 2006–2007. Ontario Ministry of Agriculture, Food and Rural Affairs, Publication no. 363, www.omafra.gov.on.ca/english/products/hort.html

2 Wallace, Janet, ed. 2001. *Organic Field Crop Handbook*. Canadian Organic Growers.

3 Nelson, K., Lynch, D., and Boiteau, G. *Soil Health in Organic Potato Systems*. Organic Agriculture Centre, Technical Bulletin E2008–22 www.organicagcentre.ca/Docs/TechnicalBulletins08/TechnicalBulletin22web_potato.pdf

4 See 2

5 OMAFRA. 2008. *Field Crop Budgets.* Publication no. 060. http://www.omafra.gov.on.ca/english/busdev/facts/pub60.htm

6 Lynch, D. From a conversation with Dr. Derek Lynch of the Organic Agriculture Centre of Canada about the research by one of his graduate students, E. Clegg.

7 PEI Ministry of Agriculture. 2000. *Agricultural Business Profile on Organic Potatoes.* www.gov.pe.ca/af/agweb/index.php3?number=atoz

8 Coleman, Eliot. 1995. *The New Organic Grower.* Old Bridge Press.

9 Sustainable Agriculture Network. 2007. *Managing Cover Crops Profitably,* Handbook Series Book 9. www.sare.org/publications/index.htm

10 See 7

11 Brown, Christine. 2007. Available Nutrients & Value for Manure from Various Livestock Types. *Nutrient Management Field Crops.* Ontario Ministry of Agriculture, Food & Rural Affairs (OMAFRA).

12 Kinsey, Neal & Walters, Charles. 2006. *Hands-On Agronomy.* Acres U.S.A.

13 Rodale, The New Farm Fact Sheet, 2003. *My-Core-What? The blow-by-blow on beneficial root fungi, mycorrhizas – rocket boosters for your plants.* www.rodaleinstitute.org

Ferme Donald Roussy

Donald Roussy, Saint Simeon, Quebec

Cash crops:
potatoes, berries and asparagus

Green manure:
none

Irrigation:
none

Soil:
stony loam, pH 7+, 134 frost free days

Farm size:
20 ha (50 ac), 0.6 ha (1.5 ac) in potatoes

History:
certified organic by Ecocert since 2005

Donald Roussy farms 20 hectares (50 ac) near Saint Siméon in the Gaspé region of Québec. In addition to 0.6 hectares (1.5 ac) in potatoes, Donald grows strawberries, raspberries and asparagus on slightly rolling fields surrounded by mature forests. While his crops and farm have been certified organic since 2005 by Ecocert Canada, Donald has been growing potatoes for only two years, producing six bushels of potatoes for each bushel planted. Donald markets his potatoes with a group of five other farmers (who also share seed potatoes). All of their produce is marketed locally.

Donald rotates potatoes with his other crops so that potatoes will return to a location only after three years have passed. Chicken manure from a neighbouring farm is used to supply fertility.

Cultivation takes place in the spring before planting. Using hand tools, Donald weeds and hills the potatoes as the season progresses. In the fall, he harvests by hand and stores the potatoes in bags until they go to market. Irrigation is not needed; soil moisture is adequate throughout the growing season.

The main pest is the Colorado potato beetle which Donald controls by hand picking. He removes the adults early to prevent the second generations from becoming established. He has tried diatomaceous earth but with little success. Diseases have not been a problem.

Annual broadleaf weeds are the main challenge. Donald controls them through spring soil preparation as well as with hand pulling during the growing season, which he notes is very labour intensive.

> Donald's advice to new organic farmers is to start small and learn to grow potatoes well before going large scale. This strategy also allows time for market development.

5 Organic Seed Potato Production

"It is a challenge between yield and disease-free. Disease-free has to come first as we are growing organic seed potatoes."
Bruce Miller

Today in Canada only a handful of farmers are growing certified organic certified seed potatoes. The cost of inspection fees and the lower return that farmers receive for seed potatoes in many parts of the country as compared to tablestock has discouraged farmers from entering into organic seed potato production. Some seed potato producers have had success selling small quantities of seed at good prices to market gardeners, but overall the market is discouraging.

The seed potato market has not grown at the same rate as organic markets generally because many farmers save their seed potatoes from year to year and some continue to buy conventional seed. Although organic farmers are required to conduct and record their search for organic seed, they are allowed to use conventional seed if organic varieties are not available.

Farms which produce certified seed potatoes are inspected by Canadian Food Inspection Agency potato seed inspectors twice during the growing season. An additional inspection may be scheduled if any problems are discovered. Inspectors look mainly for late blight, mosaic viruses and Leaf Roll Virus (PLRV). Bacterial ring rot is a concern in all regions of Canada. Core samples must be submitted for laboratory testing before receiving seed certification. Inspectors are also concerned with varietal mixing. Organic producers use long crop rotations, so volunteers from previous crops rarely occur. Still, care must be taken during planting, harvesting and storage to ensure that varieties are kept separate.

It can be difficult to have a disease-free field at the time of inspection. Roguing out plants which show signs of disease is a common strategy. In regions where the Colorado potato beetle defoliate the plants, there may not be enough leaves left for the inspector to examine for signs of disease, in which case certification may be refused.

All certified potato seed is developed in a greenhouse from disease-free tissue cultures. Each generation of seed potato grown out in the field is given a designation that identifies the number of years which have passed since the seed was generated in the greenhouse. Elite I, II and III are considered 'young' seed as the percentage of disease increases with each year it is grown out. The class designation begins with 'Nuclear', which describes the mini-tubers produced from greenhouse tissue cultures. Nuclear seed is certified to be free of disease and viral contamination.

Each generation after Nuclear has a progressively higher allowable percentage of diseased plants. If the damage exceeds the maximum limit, the inspector can assign an older class than the actual age of the seed.

'Certified' is the last generation of seed potatoes that can be sold as seed in Canada. Because each generation of seed contains more disease, identifying seed potatoes by generation helps to control viral outbreaks. To prevent seed borne diseases, many growers believe in purchasing lower generation seed. Some farmers have also found that low generation seed possesses more vigour than older seed.

Henry Ellenberger of Coe Hill, Ontario, maintains the purity of varieties grown side by side in the same year by planting four rows of sweet corn between them. He has noticed an additional benefit of intercropping: the potato rows adjacent to the corn are shaded leading to lower moisture loss and higher yields.

CLASS	GENERATION
Nuclear	Mini-tubers
Pre-Elite	1
Elite I	2
Elite II	3
Elite III	4
Elite IV	5
Foundation	6
Certified	7

On certified seed production fields, only certified seed potatoes can be grown. This reduces contamination of the soil by diseases brought in on the seed potatoes but also limits a seed producer from experimenting with heritage varieties.

Organic seed producers often purchase conventional early generation seed to establish their seed supply. While organic standards require the use of organic seed, an organic seed rule exemption application once approved can permit an exemption, provided there is no organic seed available.

Without a strong incentive to continue, Dan and Christine Vriend of August Organics in Alberta may give up seed potato production. Seed production only helps farmers if it extends their market beyond what they can sell for a premium as tablestock. Seed potato prices can be as much as 50% lower than tablestock and still the market is slack.

Ellenberger Farm

Henry & Janet Ellenberger, Coe Hill, Ontario

Cash crops:
hay, vegetables, small fruits and potatoes

Livestock:
Red Poll cattle, Duroc-Tamworth pigs, poultry

Green manure:
red clover

Irrigation:
none. Precipitation: 82 cm (32.4 in.)

Soil:
sandy, stony ground with clay underneath, 133 frost free days

Farm size:
81 ha
(200 ac) with .8 ha
(2 ac) of potatoes

History:
certified organic by OC/Pro since 2002

Henry Ellenberger

Maureen Bostock

Janet and Henry Ellenberger grow the only certified organic certified seed potatoes in Ontario. They recently moved to a farm on Ridge Road near Bancroft. Growing potatoes at their former location near Belleville was a challenge as summers were hot and isolation from herbicide and pesticide spray drift was difficult. Their new farm sits on top of a ridge, 335 metres (1100 ft) above sea level in a sparsely populated area where trees and hedges protect their crops from spray drift. While their new location is 110 km (70 miles) further north, temperatures are more moderate.

Crop rotation is the Ellenberger's most successful strategy for dealing with pests and insects. Land is taken out of forage production and put in potatoes for one year. The field is then returned to forage crops or is planted to other vegetable crops or small fruits.

In addition to potato production, Henry and Janet raise Red Poll cross cattle, Duroc-Tamworth cross pigs, poultry, sweet corn, strawberries and raspberries. They sell table potatoes, vegetables and meat through the Quinte Organic Farmers Co-op at farmers markets in Toronto. Henry and Janet hope to develop a local market with seasonal residents in the cottage country near their farm.

The soil is acidic, sandy and stony ground with a clay hardpan underneath which helps to retain moisture. At 133 days, their season is noticeably longer than it was when Henry's family farmed in the area. It used to be impossible to dig potatoes in late October, says Henry.

To maintain soil fertility, the Ellenbergers use legumes in the forage part of the rotation, and add composted manure from their cows. At planting they apply 1120 kg/ha (1000 lb/ac) of greenstone to help retain moisture, along with 168–336 kg/ha (150–300 lb/ac) of kelp to add trace elements and 5.6 kg/ha (5 lb/ac) of organic sugar to feed soil bacteria. Potato varieties include Norland, Chieftain, Onaway, Hertha, Fianna, Estema and Goldrush.

Cultivation includes blind harrowing with a chain harrow one or two weeks following emergence. Hilling is done only once during the season and the hills are kept low to preserve moisture.

Henry notes that quackgrass seems to be worse after fall plowing, compared to years when field preparation takes place in the spring. Quackgrass becomes more challenging as the harvest season progresses if the fields are wet and the potato harvest is delayed.

After digging the potatoes in the fall, Henry seeds winter rye. If the weather prevents the seeding of the fall cover crop, the following spring he plants a spring grain underseeded with red clover. The expected yield of potatoes is 12.5 tonnes per hectare (5 tons per acre).

Maureen Bostock

The storage facility consists of a 55 square metre (600 sq. ft.) building, built into a hill to provide insulation. Above it is a gambrel-roofed machine shed. The storage area can accommodate 29 tonnes (33 tons) of potatoes, stored in bins. The space is ventilated by a fan, and a space heater is used occasionally in the winter.

D & D Market Garden

Don and Donna Kizlyk, Fosston, Saskatchewan

Cash crops:
alfalfa hay, vegetables and potatoes

Green manure:
alfalfa, weeds

Irrigation:
none

Soil:
sandy, stony ground with clay underneath

Farm size:
132 ha (320 ac) with 2-4 ha (6-10 ac) in potatoes

History:
certified organic by OCIA since 2001

Don's advice for new growers: "work a season with another organic grower. Go to every field day, farm tour, research trial and marketing seminar that you can."

"You can learn a lot from books," Don says, "but you need to talk to other growers." He recommends that new farmers look at conventional fields to observe the problems other farmers deal with. "The least expensive thing you can do," he adds, "is to learn from someone else's mistakes."

Don and Donna Kizlyk farm 132 ha (320 ac) near Fosston, Saskatchewan. Of the 8 ha (20 ac) set aside for their market garden operation, 2–4 ha (6–10 ac) are in potatoes. Their crops are sold to customers who travel from all across Saskatchewan to purchase at the farm gate.

Certified organic since 2001, the Kizlyks have a traditional approach to growing potatoes. With no disease and few pest problems, they grow out their own seed year after year (Viking and Norland for twenty years and Yukon Gold for fifteen years). They believe that the plants should not be spoiled and should have to work for a living. They do not use irrigation. They accept the potato plants' preference for particular soils rather than force them to grow where it might be more convenient. To prevent the spread of disease, the Kizlyks cull any plants that look sickly.

Don believes that potato plants should have lots of air and room to grow. Rows are spaced 1.5 metres (5 ft.) apart. With his homemade ground-driven planter, he spaces the potato seed 30, 45, 50 cm (12, 18 or 20 in.) apart depending on the variety. The only input is a green manure crop of weeds which is plowed down before going to seed. He plans to intercrop marigolds between the potato rows to separate varieties and inhibit pests.

While the average rainfall in their region is 35 cm (14 in.) per year, the rainfall in 2006 and 2007 tipped the record books with 76 cm (30 in.) each year. Yields dropped to 36 tonnes per hectare (15 tons per acre). In the fall of 2007, the land was too wet for harvesting and before it could dry up, the temperatures plunged below freezing – making harvest impossible.

Don encourages wildlife in the bioreserve on his farm. One year he found a family of sharp-tailed grouse living for the summer in an area of his field where Colorado potato beetles had appeared. The grouse were eating the larvae. As a result, the beetles were controlled.

In years when the beetles are numerous, Don hand-picks them. In the fall, after the nights have started to freeze while the days are still warm, he cultivates the potato field to disturb the hibernating beetles. Awakened from hibernation, the beetles start looking for food and freeze when the temperature drops at night.

6 PLANTING & CULTIVATION

WHILE THE PLOWDOWN OF LEGUMES and application of organic nutrients are critical to producing a superior crop of organic potatoes, attention must be paid to seed piece preparation, planting and cultivation of the crop. By working with the potato tuber's unique ability to control sprouting and dormancy, seed potato vigour can be enhanced.

Maintaining a weed-free seed bed through timely cultivation and hilling is important to the success of the crop. The practice of mulching offers an alternative approach to crop maintenance while addressing a number of important challenges.

BREAKING DORMANCY

Potatoes contain a genetic code that determines the length of dormancy and an internal clock that turns on the potato's readiness to sprout. After the plant dies, there is a period of dormancy during which the tuber will not sprout even if temperature, moisture or light conditions are ideal.

Once dormancy has come to an end, there are three stages of tuber maturity: apical dominance, the multi-sprout stage and the weak, branched (hairy) sprout stage. Temperature and access to light promotes sprouting.

The first bud to sprout and break dormancy is at the apical or bud end of the potato – the end with the most eyes. These eyes possess apical dominance in that, initially, they prevent the eyes in the rest of the tuber from sprouting. If a tuber is planted at apical dominance, there will be few main stems on the plant and only a few tubers will set. While the yield may be lower, planting at apical dominance can be useful to produce an early crop of new potatoes.

At the multi-sprout stage, short stout sprouts appear randomly on the tuber. Whole seed or seed pieces planted at this stage produce the most vigorous plants, set the highest number of tubers and possess the vigour to resist viral infections.

Over-mature tubers have weak, branched (hairy) sprouts and will not produce healthy plants. Because of the potato's internal clock, the plants will mature before tuber production peaks, resulting in lower yields of smaller potatoes.

Potato seed preparation

A few simple preventive measures in seed preparation can eliminate some of the vectors of disease and get the plants off to a good start.

On an organic farm, it is better to plant whole, rather than cut, seed potatoes. However, if it is necessary to cut the seed potatoes, they should be warmed to 10°C (50°F) before cutting into pieces. Rotten tubers should be discarded. Plant vigour is enhanced if the seed weighs between 35 and 60 grams (1–2 oz). Smaller pieces are slower to emerge, have less vigour, and are more likely to decay. Seed pieces that are too large bind up in the planter, resulting in bruises which can become infected with soil-borne diseases. Check mechanical seed piece cutters to ensure that the sizer is adjusted properly to produce the preferred seed piece size; keep cutting blades sharp.

When all the eyes are concentrated at the apical end, a characteristic of varieties such as Jemseg and Yukon Gold, tubers should be cut by hand, so that pieces with no eyes (called blind pieces) can be discarded.

Cut seed should be handled carefully to prevent bruising and should not be washed. Once the cut surfaces are healed, the cut seed should be planted. Exposure to hot sun or drying wind may cause the tubers to develop cracks, increasing susceptibility to bacteria and fungi.

If they cannot be planted right away, the seed pieces should be stored at temperatures between 10–15°C (50–59°F), with 90–95% humidity and forced air blown onto the pile. Conditions should be maintained for three to four days. The temperature can be lowered, but humidity should stay high until planted.

Chitting

Chitting (green sprouting) is the process of maturing seed in light conditions to produce a premature end to dormancy and early sprout growth. Chitting is used where early emergence and yield are important, as in short season areas, and can result in a gain of up to fourteen days on the growing season.

Chitting should be undertaken when temperatures of 8°C (46°F) can be maintained for several weeks. Small whole seed is placed in shallow pans, two to three tubers deep, allowing for air movement and light penetration. Pans can be placed under fluorescent lights or in natural light conditions in a temperature-controlled greenhouse. Chitting produces stubby dark green sprouts which are vigorous and unlikely to be damaged during planting.

Jim Gerritsen of WoodPrairie Farm green sprouts 15 tons of seed potatoes each spring. Thirty days before planting, the seed potatoes are exposed to 21–23.8°C (70–75°F) temperatures while kept in the dark. At the end of the first week, defective potatoes are graded out and the remainder are placed on sprouting trays (45 x 71 x 10 cm / 18 x 28 x 4 in) stacked on pallets nine high. The temperature is reduced to 10–13°C (50–55°F) and the potatoes are exposed to sunlight, fluorescent or incandescent light. The light ensures that the sprout does not elongate. Should that occur, the temperature is decreased to 7°C (45°F) or the intensity of light is increased. After three weeks in the trays, the seed is planted. Gaining ten to fourteen days enables Jim to grow out late varieties of potatoes. If insect or disease pressure is heavy, the crop can be harvested early and the yields will still be good. After harvesting new potatoes, Jim can plant a second crop in the same location and still get an adequate yield despite his short growing season in Northern Maine.

Planting

"Talk to the old-timers and ask them how their parents grew potatoes. Many of the old-timers wouldn't plant 'til the end of May or the beginning of June, instead of the end of April. Tools have made us disregard the limitations of the potato plant. We have to go back to the basic rules."

Marcus Koenig

Ideally, potato seed should be planted as soon as the soil has warmed up, unless you are delaying planting until mid-June to control Colorado potato beetle damage. If soil is hot and dry, the seed pieces can dry up. In cold, wet soil, germination can be delayed and tubers may rot.

Planting should be delayed for two weeks after plowing down a heavy green stand of rye or clover. Nutrient imbalances can occur and the process of decomposition favours disease organisms. As well, nutrients are tied up as microorganisms work to break down the material.

Plant seed potatoes 8–13 cm (3–5 in.) beneath the surface. Shallow planting may result in sporadic germination and tuber greening. If planted too deep, emergence may be delayed and plants may have less vigour.

Approximately 1,800 kg of seed is required to plant 1 hectare (1600 lb/ ac) with the typical row spacing of 90 cm (36 in.).

Spacing of potato plants in the row vary with the variety. Wider spacing of 30–32 cm (12–13 in.) is suitable for varieties with a heavy tuber set, smooth tubers and resistance to hollow heart. Closer spacing of 15–20 cm (6–8 in.) is recommended for varieties with a lower tuber set or susceptibility to producing rough, oversized tubers or hollow heart.

Maureen Bostock

Picks are the most common style of pick-up on potato planters

Cultivation and hilling

"It is useful to remember that potatoes are a tough plant; even if they have been buried by harrowing they will re-emerge."
Isaiah Swidersky

Weed pressure on organic potato farms can be reduced by a long and diverse crop rotation. Weeds are highly adapted and those that prefer an open canopy and row crop environment can be smothered by competitive forage plants in the alternate years of the rotation.

Once the seed potatoes are planted, timely cultivation is important as it is most effective when the weeds are at the first emergence or white hair stage. After the hills have been formed, the cultivator width can be set to straddle the hills to allow for continued cultivation between the rows until the canopy closes over the row.

Losses in yield attributed to weed competition in potato crops can be significant. For example, one study noted that three weeks of competition from weeds can reduce the yield of potatoes by as much as thirty percent. [1]

Recent studies have shown that plants become 'aware' of weeds very early in their germination and respond by turning away from the weed to protect their access to light. Energy is diverted from root production, which is central to the health of the plant, and redirected to producing increased height. This net energy loss reduces plant vigour and the plants' ability to respond to stresses that come along throughout the growing season.[2]

Isaiah Swidersky of Rose Mountain Farm prepares the field in spring by tilling the land before planting. After planting, he blind harrows one or two times, hills, and harrows again after emergence. Depending on the field, the crop is harrowed and hilled again just before the canopy closes.

Following initial cultivation and planting, prior to emergence, blind harrowing is often used. A rod weeder, an inverted diamond tooth harrow or a flame weeder is taken over the field to kill emerging weeds, leaving the potato seed intact. Cultivators (rod weeders or finger weeders) deposit weed seeds on the surface of the soil. Weed seeds on the surface are vulnerable to an early break in dormancy and exposure to moisture which reduces seed viability. Birds and insects (crickets in particular), consume large amounts of these seeds and reduce the build-up of the weed seed bank in the soil.

Hiller design can affect the ability of the hill to protect the potato crop. A hiller which forms a less uniform hill can reduce run-off during heavy rains and improve water infiltration. High wide hills minimize the exposure of tubers to late blight spores washed down from infected plants. Low wide hills preserve moisture.

Derek Lynch

Hilling is an effective weed control strategy

Repeated hilling is recommended if heavy rains have caused compaction or exposed the tubers; however, hilling should be avoided late in the growing season to minimize root pruning.

Once the canopy has closed, the field will be relatively free of weeds for the remainder of the season unless the canopy is thinned because of leafhopper damage or disease. In this situation, heavy weed growth may result and can cause problems at harvest.

WEEDS

Maureen Bostock

Quackgrass infestation in the fall

QUACKGRASS

While many weeds can affect yields, quackgrass reduces the yield and damages the potato crop by piercing tubers with its root stolons. A minor quackgrass presence in the field can become a damaging invasion following defoliation by insects or disease. Quackgrass is also called couchgrass or twitchgrass.

In cold winters, fall plowing can kill most quackgrass roots. It should be followed in the spring with shallow cultivation using a finger weeder, cultivator or digger to bring roots that survived the winter to the surface to dry. The CMN Couch Grass Killer is an implement designed to kill quackgrass.[3] It is fitted with a slow moving pick-up reel which rotates in the opposite direction to the forward motion of the tractor. The pick-up agitates the soil lightly, separating roots that are then deposited on the surface.

A short fallow in late July or August of the year before potatoes can be useful strategy. The field of quackgrass can be disked, harrowed repeatedly, and later planted in a competitive green manure crop.[4] On its own, disking can amplify the problem as quackgrass rhizomes continue to grow even after being cut.

OBSERVING WEEDS

Ehrenfried Pfeiffer viewed weeds as "specialists [which] resist conditions such as drought, acidity of soil, lack of humus, mineral deficiencies as well as one-sidedness of minerals."[5]

Observing weeds can help organic farmers understand their soil. Pfeiffer classified weeds into three categories:

- highly acidic soils: sorrels, docks, horsetails, hawkweed and knapweed
- hardpan or crust formation: mustards, horse nettle, penny cress, morning glory, quackgrass and chamomile
- cultivation: lamb's quarters, plantain, chickweed, buttercup, dandelion, nettle

Weeds are adapted to very specific environmental conditions, establishing to fill a niche left open by either cultivation or soil imbalances. Each species occupies a niche and then dies back, rebalancing the soil. For example, lamb's quarters will establish quickly when there is excess nitrogen needing to be taken up.

Taproot species, such as dandelions and thistles, can break through the plowpan layer of the soil, repair the soil structure, and bring minerals up from the subsoil. As their taproots decompose, they leave channels which are used by soil life, including earthworms, to travel through the soil.

MULCH

Mulching has many advantages, particularly for the small farmer. Overall, mulches can increase yields and improve soil quality. Specifically, a mulch of several inches can:

- reduce pest movement and egg laying
- create a barrier between the soil borne diseases and plants
- hold moisture high in the soil, maintain consistent soil moisture and reduce evaporation
- enhance soil biological activity
- suppress weeds
- add organic matter
- moderate soil temperature

Mulching materials include straw, partially rotted hay, leaves, paper and newsprint (using soy inks and no glossy photographs). The Canadian Organic Standards require the use of organic mulch materials. Straw, for example, must be from organic grain fields because conventionally grown straw may contain residues of herbicides used to kill the grain prematurely a few days before harvest.

Mulches can reduce problems with the Colorado potato beetle. The mulch can harbour predatory spiders which can reduce Colorado potato beetle numbers significantly. The beetles are also discouraged by the physical barrier of the mulch which limits their movement.

For a number of years, Hida Manns has been conducting research on the impact of mulching on insect predators and soil health at her farm in Kendal, Ontario. Hida spreads hay mulch on the field in the fall. In the spring, she adds another layer of coarse mulch, and then plants the potatoes under it (on the untilled soil surface). By the time she trims the tall grass between the beds, the potato plants are 30–45 cm (12–18 in.) high and well established without any beetle pressure. When the plants die back, there is a bumper crop of potatoes and 5 cm (2 in.) of crumbly soil/mulch material covering the soil. Hida has observed many glistening spider webs near the ground, along with larger orb weaver nests in the top foliage.

While some pests may be discouraged by mulch, it is an ideal habitat for slugs. Living with slugs might be an acceptable trade-off given the benefits associated with an increase in the numbers of beneficial organisms.

Mulching the potato crop precludes mechanical harvesting unless the mulch is removed before harvest. However, overall, mulching contributes to long-term soil health and is an excellent choice for small fields.

Irrigation

Potatoes require 2 cm (1 in.) of water per week at tuber set and during the period after flowering when the tubers are formed and begin to size up. In some parts of Canada, natural rainfall is sufficient; in other regions, irrigation is necessary to support yields. Soil moisture levels should be maintained at a point halfway between soil capacity and the level at which wilting is permanent. Too much water before tuber initiation can lead to nutrient leaching, increased disease and tuber abnormalities.

Managing irrigation requires knowing your soil type and its capacity to hold water, as well as understanding how your crops store water. Care should be taken to stop irrigating a few weeks before harvest to prevent late blight.

A soil-building program which includes cover crops and compost applications can increase organic matter in the soil which, in turn, helps the soil retain moisture. Forty-five kilograms (100 lb.) of soil with an organic matter (OM) content of 1½–2 % OM can hold 15–20 kg (35–45 lb.) of water, the equivalent of 1–4 cm (½ to 1½ in.) of rain. If the OM content is raised to 4–5%, the soil is able to hold 74–88 kg (165–195 lb.) of water which is the equivalent of 4–6 inches of rain.[6]

The Canadian Organic Standards require that organic products must be protected from sources of contamination. Water sources may become contaminated by intensive livestock operations, by seismic or construction events which impact the integrity of the aquifer, or by wildlife. Testing irrigation sources (well, pond or streams) on the farm ensures that the water is potable and meets standards for drinking water. Irrigation systems range from drip irrigation (which has the lowest rate of loss through evaporation) to overhead spray systems.

FOOTNOTES

1 Ivany, Jerry A. 2002. *Physical Weed Control in Potatoes.* 5th EWRS Workshop on Physical Weed Control, Pisa Italy.

2 Swanton, Clarence. *Integrated Weed Management Strategies for Organic Farmers.* Presentation at Guelph Organic Conference, January 2008.

3 www.cmn.dk/indexuk.htm

4 Duval, Jean. Controlling Quackgrass. ***The Canadian Organic Grower,*** Summer 2006.

5 Pfeiffer, Ehrenfried E. 1970. ***Weeds and What They Tell.*** Biodynamic Farming & Gardening Association.

6 Kinsey, N. & Walters, C. 2006. *Hands-On Agronomy.* Acres USA.

Wild Blue Yonder Farm

Garret Gillespie and Heidi Marion, Tagish, Yukon

Cash crops:
hay, vegetables and potatoes

Livestock:
cattle, goats

Green manure:
alfalfa, weeds

Irrigation:
overhead sprinkler. Average precipitation: less than 200 mm (8 in.)

Soil:
silty loam

Farm size:
89 ha (220 ac), .8–2 ha (2-5 ac) of potatoes

History:
certified organic by OCIA since 2001

Garret Gillespie and Heidi Marion have been described as the most successful vegetable producers among the Yukon's organic pioneers. Organic farming in the Yukon is on the verge of expansion as consumers become more educated about food choices and seek locally produced, healthy food.

Farming operations at Wild Blue Yonder Farm were suspended in 2008 to give Garret and Heidi time to rethink their approach. They plan to reshape their farm around horse farming, based on their view that using horses, instead of a diesel tractor, is not only preparing for the future but making a significant contribution towards it by reducing fossil fuel use.

Wild Blue Yonder Farm consists of 89 hectares (220 acres) of silt-loam soil with thirty head of cattle, a herd of meat goats, hay and pasture, and 4 hectares (10 acres) of market vegetables including 0.8 to 2 hectares (2–5 acres) of potatoes (depending on the year).

Garret follows the teachings of Dr. William A. Albrecht, seeking to balance soil nutrients and support soil biology to feed the plants. For example, maintaining the balance of calcium to magnesium is primary to growing healthy crops. Garret attributes the taste and nutritional value of their potatoes to their soil fertility program, the natural fertility of soil, and the climate. Yields range between 15 and 49 tonnes per hectare (6 to 19 tons per acre). Norland, Yukon Gold, and Fingerlings are their main varieties.

Garret and Heidi's soil program has evolved since the first year when they experienced a total crop failure as a result of calcium deficiency. They came to understand the limitations of their soil by observing the weeds that thrived – arnica and larkspur – and those which would not grow at all, such as lambsquarters. In their crop rotation, potatoes follow the plowdown of cover crops of either sweetclover or red clover.

Garret and Heidi apply mature compost at the rate of 13.4 tonnes per hectare (6 tons/acre) to compensate for the relative lack of mycorrhizal fungi in the soil. They also apply limestone from a nearby quarry at a rate of 10 tonnes/ha (4.4 tons/ac), providing both calcium and micronutrients (sulphur, copper, boron and iron) which occur naturally in this mineral deposit. Potatoes are followed in the rotation by carrots, then brassicas and lettuce.

The Tagish region has a moderate climate compared to regions of the Yukon that have killing frosts in July. The area is very dry with less than 220 mm (8.6 in.) of precipitation per year, mostly in the form of snow. Garret uses an overhead sprinkler to irrigate the crop. Potato seed is planted at a depth of 10 cm (4 in.) where there is sufficient moisture to get them started. By mid-June if it gets hot (30 °C/86 °F) and windy, they begin to irrigate weekly. Soils are left rough and trashy over the winter, and are protected by snow cover. This helps to prevent erosion if a fast spring break up occurs.

Potatoes are planted around the last week of May and harvesting begins with new potatoes around the 3rd week of August. Potatoes are hilled three or four times throughout the season to provide good weed control. Harvest continues until the end of October.

Using well established cover crops and weed management during the potato phase of the rotation, Garret and Heidi are able to control most weeds. As the soil fertility improves, the weed species – the unintended crop – changes from weeds showing deficiencies to lambsquarters "big enough to tie a horse to." Successful weed control measures include flaming immature weeds early in the season and cultivating between the hills with the disk hiller set to run shallowly (just turning the soil between the rows) followed by hilling.

As the Yukon climate is inhospitable to most pests and diseases, the Millers rarely have problems, unless disease comes on imported potato seed. As a preventive practice, the Millers use certified organic certified seed potatoes.

Garret's advice to new organic potato growers is to keep the acreage small and the farm diversified. In northern climates, weather can "get in the way of the crop and if you are heavily invested you can go bankrupt," he says. "Diversification ensures that if one crop fails, you have something else to fall back on."

7 DISEASE & PEST PREVENTION

"Because we cannot control the leafhoppers, we have to make the plant strong to resist their feeding."
Marcus Koenig

THERE IS NO SILVER BULLET for controlling pests on organic farms. Organic agriculture is based on producing food in a balanced relationship with other inhabitants of our environment and requires a holistic approach to pest management that uses preventive measures and low-impact substances.

Curiously, organic farmers report less pest and disease pressure than conventional producers, suggesting that organic methods successfully foster healthy plants because the plants grow in balanced soils. Healthy plants are less attractive to pests and able to resist diseases.

Nonetheless there are challenges. Pest pressure may develop as a result of:

- regional pest problems
- the direction of prevailing winds
- seed potatoes imported onto the farm

PREVENTIVE PRACTICES

Awareness of potential problems allows the organic farmer to plan control measures including:

- crop rotation with potatoes grown one year out of four to reduce the problems associated with soil-borne pathogens
- adequate fertility (vigorous plants resist disease)
- sufficient but not excessive levels of nitrogen – the latter produces abundant top growth and results in increased humidity and a blight-prone environment
- cultivation to control weeds to decrease humidity
- seedstock that is healthy low-generation certified seed to avoid transmitting disease from contaminated seed pieces
- whole seed used for planting if possible
- alignment of potato rows with prevailing winds to prevent wind transfer of fungal spores to adjacent rows

- irrigation during the day so plants can dry off before the temperature drops at night
- avoiding irrigation late in the season to prevent late blight

FIELD INSPECTION

Twice a week fields should be inspected. Infected plants should be pulled, bagged and buried. Problem areas should be marked and rechecked for signs of spreading of the disease. It is useful to disk under any late blight hot-spots immediately to prevent the spread of the infection to healthy plants. Cultivate to seal soil cracks and reduce the spread of late blight to potato tubers during rainy weather. When the weather is wet, look for signs of late blight, blackleg, aerial stem rot, white mould, pink rot or other fungal diseases. Also, check low, wet spots in the fields for diseased plants.

DISEASE RECOGNITION

The distribution pattern of leaf symptoms in the field can help to diagnose the problem:

- Circular patterns of affected plants may be attributed to aphid or nematode infestations.
- Early blight will affect most of the plants in the field if the plants were already under stress (e.g. drought) but if the source of the infection is seed borne, you may see leaf symptoms scattered through the field.
- Lightning strikes can result in sudden plant death, while disease symptoms spread from a few plants to the whole field.
- Physiological leaf roll resulting from plant stress (e.g. drought, nutrient deficiencies or flooding) can be distinguished from Potato Leaf Roll Virus (PLRV) as the leaves affected by PLRV have a leathery consistency.

HARVEST

If late blight symptoms appear in the field, tuber infection can be reduced by delaying harvest for two weeks after the top growth dies.

STORAGE

Optimal storage conditions reduce the incidence of storage-related disease. Sort tubers coming into storage and discard diseased tubers. Keep the temperature as low as possible to prevent spread of diseases. Destroy cull potatoes by burial, composting, field incorporation or using as livestock feed before next year's crop emerges.

BENEFICIAL INSECTS IN THE POTATO FIELD

Organic farmers value beneficial insects and other organisms because of their ability to pollinate crops and/or prey on pests. Beneficial insects can either be purchased for release or attracted to the farm by providing appropriate habitat, such as season-long pollen and nectar sources along field borders or strips within the field. Scouting fields can help farmers increase their familiarity with local beneficial organisms, as well as pests.

Beneficial insects may be harmed by the use of organic pest control products which kill more than the target species. Some farmers use perimeter sprays – applying pest control products to one sprayer-width on the borders of the field, rather than applying it to the whole field. This protects beneficials which might be harmed by the pest control product. To keep beneficial insects in the field requires leaving a small population of pests to provide food for the beneficials. The goal of organic management is to maintain the balance between predator and pest.

Insectary strips are rows of plants in a field that provide habitat for beneficial organisms and provide an alternative food source to sustain the organisms when pest numbers are low. For example, corridors of flowering plants every 50-100 metres (165 to 330 ft.) in a field can increase the mobility of beneficial insects within the field. [1]

Lacy Phacelia (*Phacelia tanacetifolia*) is a valuable plant for use in insectary strips because it has a long flowering period and is drought-resistant. It is sown at a rate of 6.6-11 kg/ha (3-5 lb/ac) on its own or as 40 % of a mixture of other flowering plants such as borage, buckwheat, bachelor's buttons, dill, alyssum, Queen Anne's lace or legumes.

Natural predators reduce pest populations but do not always provide adequate control. Hand picking or other benign methods of control are complementary as they do not interfere with the beneficials.

Encouraging biodiversity does more than reduce pest pressure. A healthy insect population, for example, also supports bats and birds which exert tremendous influence in maintaining the balance of prey (i.e. pests) and predators.

Predatory insects can be purchased for release to boost the natural population. Success with release programs depends on a number of factors such as:

- providing the appropriate habitat
- timing the release to ensure there is food available
- following the storage and release directions provided by the supplier

PEST	PREDATOR	LATIN NAME
Aphids	parasitic wasps	*Aphelinus abdominalis* *Aphidius colemani* *Aphidius ervi*
	minute pirate bugs	*Orius* spp
	green lacewings	*Chrysoperla* spp
	ladybeetles	*Coccinellidae* spp.
Leafhoppers	minute pirate bugs	*Orius* spp
	parasitic wasps	*Anagrus atomus*
Colorado potato beetles	two-spotted stink bug	*Perillus bioculatus*
	spined soldier bug	*Podisus maculiventris*

Ladybeetles (ladybugs) are a major predator of potato aphids. Ladybug larvae have a dark brown to black alligator appearance, and, like all beneficials, should be protected when found in the field. Another aphid predator is the green lacewing, which can consume up to 200 aphids per week. Parasitic wasps control potato aphids. For example, releases of *Aphidius colemani* and *Aphidius ervi* can control green peach and cotton aphids, and *Anagrus atomus* is reported to be an effective predator against leafhoppers.

Minute pirate bugs feed on potato aphids and leafhopper nymphs. Alfalfa and early flowering plants provide minute pirate bugs with food until their preferred diet of insects is available. To supplement natural populations of pirate bugs, 5,000 to 12,000 bugs must be released per hectare (2,000–4,000 bugs per acre).

Spined soldier bugs are shield-shaped, black-specked, brown 1 cm (½ in.) bugs with sharp points on the shoulders. The nymphs are similar but wingless. When the nymphs hatch, they consume water or plant juices for a short period before becoming predators. There may be one or two generations per year depending on the location. The spined soldier bug attacks prey by impaling it and sucking its bodily fluids.

Two-spotted stink bugs are voracious consumers of Colorado potato beetle larvae and eggs. They are 1 cm (0.4 in.) long, have the outline of a cow's head on the back and two black spots on bright yellow, orange or red shoulders (technically the thoracic segment called the pronotum).

Susie Osler

Two-spotted stink bug (left) with its prey, potato bug larvae

General predators such as spiders and ground beetles eat many pests including Colorado potato beetle larvae. Hedges and insectary strips provide habitat that allow these organisms to flourish.

Cultivating habitat which supports naturally occurring beneficial organisms often proves to be more cost-effective than purchasing insects for release in large potato fields. If not timed properly or appropriate habitat is not available, the released organisms may perish or simply fly away. Whenever beneficials are introduced, appropriate habitat must be provided to sustain their populations. An effective strategy to control a range of pests is to provide a diverse habitat which can sustain a diverse population of beneficial organisms including birds, bats and insects throughout the year.

FOOTNOTES

1 Altieri, Miguel A.et al. 2005. *Manage Insects on your Farm: A Guide to Ecological Strategies.* Sustainable Agriculture Network.

Klondyke Farms

Marcus Koenig, Grand Bend, Ontario

Cash crops:
alfalfa hay, soybeans, corn, potatoes

Livestock:
Tamworth pigs, cow/calf

Green manure:
alfalfa, red clover

Irrigation:
centre pivot type

Soil:
sandy to heavy Brookston clay, pH 7.2–7.8

Farm size:
303 ha (750 ac) with 8-20 ha (20-50 ac) in potatoes

History:
certified organic by CSI since 2006

Marcus Koenig farms 303 ha (750 ac) near Grand Bend in south western Ontario. He grows 8–20 ha (20–50 ac) in organic potatoes each year as well as 100 ha (250 ac) in corn, 40 ha (100 ac) in soybeans, 100 ha (250 ac) in alfalfa hay and 40 ha (100 ac) in small grains. He also raises rare Tamworth pigs and has a cow/calf operation finishing on grass. The farm began transitioning in 2001 and became fully certified organic in 2006. Over the years, potato yields have averaged 120 cwts or 13.4 tonnes per hectare (6 tons/ac).

For fresh chipping Marcus prefers the Atlantic variety. For tablestock sales, he uses Estima, Agria and Penta, which are yellow varieties from European breeding programs.

Rotation begins with fields that have been in alfalfa for three years. Alfalfa is key to his soil program; it adds organic matter and improves soil tilth. Alfalfa is followed by small grains underseeded with red clover. Marcus then uses some of the fields for potatoes, while others are seeded to corn underseeded with a combination of red clover, Italian ryegrass and vetch. If there is enough time to seed it before September 10th, barley follows potatoes; otherwise, the field is seeded to soybeans in the spring.

"We place as much emphasis on the cover crop as we do on the crop, particularly in the grain portion of the rotation," says Marcus. The soil is worked when the red clover is plowed down and followed by either rye on the sandy soils, or fall wheat or spelt on the heavy soil.

Because winter barley is a host for a fungus that causes stem lesions in subsequent crops of rye or wheat, winter barley is always followed by corn underseeded with legumes.

Several diseases are common to wheat, barley and rye. None of these grains should follow one another.

Spring field preparation involves lightly working the soil with a rolling basket style harrow (13.5-metre / 45-ft. width) with buster bars in front. This is repeated 5 or 6 times, while levelling the soil in front of the harrows to produce a fine seed bed with a crumb layer on the surface. The crumb layer prevents moisture from wicking off the soil surface by disrupting the capillary effect, an important consideration in the hot summers of south-western Ontario. One pass with the PTO-driven power harrow completes the soil preparation before planting.

Inputs are applied in the rows at planting. The formula is still being refined, but Marcus applies 330–560 kg/ha (300–500 lb/ac) of a dry pelletized mix including calcium, rock phosphate, potassium, trace elements, kelp, molasses and humates. The potatoes are inoculated with mycorrhizal fungal spores at a rate of 5 kg (11 lb) for each 4.5 metric tonne (5 ton) planter load.

Soil corrections are made the previous fall; Marcus applies 4.5–6.3 metric tonnes (5–7 tons) of finished compost with added calcium and rock phosphate to the fields.

Following plant tissue sampling, Marcus carries out a foliar feeding program to correct deficiencies and to support vigorous plant growth from tuber initiation until the end of the growing season. The program includes fish fertilizer (if plant nitrogen is low), kelp to supply micronutrients, and humates. Manganese (manganese sulphate), boron (Solubor), silica (in the form of diatomaceous earth), copper (copper sulphate) and citric acid (to adjust pH to between 5 and 6.4) are added if needed.

Hills are formed upon planting. These are worked down shallowly with the harrow until the potato sprout emerges. Marcus believes that potatoes in an organic environment respond to aggressive cultivation. The last harrowing knocks off the first sprout that appears. The second sprout has improved vigour, resulting in a greater yield as well as resistance to disease and pests.

In a separate pass, the soil is worked deeply between the hills with a 5-shank spring tine S-cultivator/scuffler, providing weed-free, loose soil to rebuild the hills.

The last hilling is delayed until the potatoes are four inches high. The plowshare shape of the Harriston hiller has a gentle action which pushes the soil up around the plant, instead of throwing it over the way the disk-style hiller does. The canopy fills in quickly and discourages emerging weeds such as pigweed and lamb's quarters. Perennial weeds such as quackgrass have not been a problem because of the well planned crop rotation.

The Pest Management Regulatory Agency (PMRA) is developing a more efficient, less rigorous registration process for low-risk botanicals which should speed up registrations.

Potatoes are planted around May 24th and harvesting begins August 10th, weather permitting. If necessary, plants are top-killed with a flail chopper although Marcus notes that in a weedy year, the weeds go through the harvester better if they are not chopped. In future, he would like to add a pass with flamers or apply copper to the residue for added disease control.

Colorado potato beetles are not a problem but one year, Marcus had to spray the perimeter with spinosad. He notes that the beetles appear to eat only the weak plants, distinguishing healthy plants with a high Brix reading of 9 from those which are weak with a Brix reading of 3–6.

Marcus has found spinosad to be ineffective against leafhoppers. He has also tried garlic spray and a foliar spray of diatomaceous earth with little success. Neem oil is reported to be effective. Marcus has expressed his frustration with the slow registration of botanicals by Canada's Pest Management Regulatory Agency.

Leafhoppers can cause tip burn, reduced yields and premature dieback of potato plants. This can result in an extremely weedy field at harvest due to the loss of the canopy. Leafhoppers are worse when the weather turns hot early in the summer. Some years they arrive weekly by the millions on southerly warm winds that precede a low pressure front.

"While soil-building practices ensure fertility for future cropping," says Marcus, "disease and pest management and weed control are the most important aspects of potato production to provide income."

8 The challenge: pests

Colorado potato beetles *(Leptinotarsa decemlineata)*

DESCRIPTION

Adult potato bug

Potato bug larva

Susie Osler

Originating in Colorado, the original hosts for the Colorado potato beetle (CPB) were wild members of the Solanacae family, which includes buffalo burr, silver leaf nightshade, black henbane, horse nettle and tobacco. As potato production increased, the beetle moved over to the potato crop. The beetles crossed the Mississippi River in 1865 and the Atlantic Ocean to Europe in 1901, likely transported in a load of potatoes. [1]

Today, Colorado potato beetles inhabit the temperate zones of most continents. In North America, the Rocky Mountains remain an impassable barrier and the West Coast remains free of CPB. The beetle cannot survive in severe northern climates as its northern limit is 54–56 degrees latitude. In some parts of Canada, beetle pressure is insignificant except for occasional population spikes; while in other areas such as the Maritimes, they are a major problem. Unfortunately, due to its adaptability and the effects of global warming, the Colorado potato beetle is expanding its northern frontier and entomologists predict that the beetle will be able to adapt to any region where potatoes can be grown.

The Colorado potato beetle will not survive if the soil temperature remains at -12°C (11°F) for a few days, at a hibernation depth of 30 cm. High mortality (88 %) of beetles has been reported when air temperatures reach -30°C (-22°F). Beetles survive better in sandy soils than in clay as sandy soils have better drainage and oxygen levels.[2] While the beetles acclimatize well if temperatures fall continuously and snow provides an insulating layer, mid-winter thaws of 7°C (45°F) for a few days can increase mortality as hibernation is interrupted.

The Colorado potato beetle emerges in spring, as late as June in some locations. Beetles that wintered well have the strength to fly, while weaker beetles walk to the potato field. The beetles feed on all members of the Solanacae family, including tomatoes, peppers and eggplants. Scouting should begin two weeks after the crop emerges.

Instar is a larval stage between moults

The females lay up to 1000 eggs during their lifespan of 4 to 5 weeks. Eggs hatch within 4–9 days. The first instar or larval stage feed for 2 to 3 weeks and then moult. The fourth instar larvae pupate in the soil for 5 to 9 days and emerge as a second generation of adults. This is the generation which overwinters in most locations.[3]

The feeding habits of the Colorado potato beetle have been the subject of a recent study in Atlantic Canada and some remarkable results have been noted:[4]

- Adult beetles spent less time feeding on organic fields than on conventional fields, with two to five times less foliage consumed.
- The number of second instar larvae levelled off earlier in plants which received moderate fertility amendments when compared to plants which received higher levels of amendments.
- The numbers of larvae were highest on the plants that received the highest rate of organic amendments.
- The third instar peaked earlier on plants which had no or low amendments, as compared to the plants which received higher amendments.

The study also demonstrated that Colorado potato beetles will abandon older, flowering potato plants in favour of younger plants, confirming the potential for a trap crop approach. A trap crop of potatoes could be planted three weeks after the main crop. The beetles should migrate to the trap crop in search of young foliage and leave the main crop to mature undisturbed. The trap crop is then destroyed by flaming along with the beetles it harbours.

Colorado potato beetles require access to healthy potato leaves following the emergence of the second generation of beetles to prepare for hibernation.

IMPACT

The beetle and larvae defoliate the plants, reducing yield and killing the plants. One adult or larvae per plant is enough to cause significant damage. Potato plants can handle 20 % defoliation when young, 40 % defoliation between early bloom and after full bloom, and 60 % defoliation from tuber formation until harvest.

Dan Vriend's strategy to control Colorado potato beetles is to drive the tractor with a 3-point hitch toolbar down the rows of plants to knock the beetles off the plants. He does this twice a day for three days as soon as they emerge from hibernation. The beetles become exhausted and stop feeding. Dan also relies on his rotation and the health of his soil to produce plants which can resist insect pressure.

Don Kizlyk takes advantage of the beetle's vulnerability early in hibernation. In the fall, after the temperature drops below freezing at night while the days are still warm, he cultivates the potato field, disturbing the hibernating beetles. The beetles start looking for food and freeze when the temperature drops again.

STRATEGIES

Crop Rotation

One study reported that only 20 % of beetles survived the trip to fields located 800 metres from previous potato fields while 50 % of beetles arrived at fields 300 metres away.[5] Exceptionally warm spring weather has been found to increase beetle activity, thereby reducing the distance effect.

Removing Vines Before Harvest

By mowing the vines before harvest, the second generation of beetles (which is preparing to hibernate) lose their food source. This reduces the overwintering population at the site. Vines can be dehydrated by flaming, a practice which has become popular with many farmers for the additional benefit of disease prevention.

Mulching

A ten-centimetre (four- inch) deep mulch has been shown to reduce beetle activity, egg production and the numbers of beetles which overwinter. For best results, apply the mulch at crop emergence. Mulch also hosts beneficial organisms, improves soil tilth and conserves moisture. Research into living mulches has shown the potential to reduce Colorado potato beetles by interfering with their ability to travel. While there are different approaches to establishing living mulches, care should be taken to ensure that the living mulch does not compete with the potatoes for nutrients or moisture and compromise potato yields.[6]

Floating Row Covers

Floating row covers can be kept in place on the plants for the whole season as potatoes do not require pollination. The row covers prevent adult females from laying eggs. The disadvantage is that the covers need to be removed for cultivation and hilling, and then reinstalled. Row covers should be set in place before adult Colorado potato beetles emerge from hibernation.

Perimeter Barriers

Plastic or metal troughs can be laid in furrows around the field perimeter to catch the beetles as they enter the field. The perimeter trap is effective against the beetles which are walking to the new crop. The beetles fall in and cannot climb the slippery sides of the troughs provided that the angle of the walls is greater than forty-six degrees. A fifty percent reduction in adults entering the field can be achieved with a perimeter barrier.[7] The beetles can then be swept up and drowned in soapy water or, if the perimeter barrier is made of black plastic mulch, the beetles are killed by the high heat.

Install the perimeter trap one week before adults emerge from hibernation. The trench should be 30–60 cm (12–24 in.) deep and 15–60 cm (6–24 in.) wide at the top. The trench can be either U- or V-shaped with the side walls sloping between 65 and 90 degrees. The top of the trench should be level with the soil.[8]

Mowed strips of fall rye around the field perimeter can act as a perimeter barrier. It also provides a habitat for beneficial organisms which prey on the Colorado potato beetles, larvae and eggs.

Barry Hiltz, Ross Farm Museum, Nova Scotia

The Potato Bug Destroyer was developed in P.E.I. in the late 19th century

Hand Picking and Vacuuming

Hand picking is a good strategy for small fields. The beetles and larvae can be knocked off the leaves into a bucket of soapy water. Soap breaks the surface tension of the water and the beetles will sink and drown. Egg masses and larvae too small to be knocked off should be crushed. Colorado potato beetle eggs are clusters of bright yellow ovals, standing on end, laid on the undersides of upper leaves. Avoid crushing egg masses or larvae of beneficial organisms.

Colorado potato beetles and larvae are easily spotted on sunny warm days. On cool and windy days, beetles hide under the leaves. Egg masses are easiest to spot on windy days when the undersides of the leaves are exposed.

Attempts to make this laborious task easier have been tried for many years. Vacuuming has been tried with mixed success. Unfortunately, the vacuum is indiscriminate and picks up many types of organisms including beneficials. Vacuuming does not pick up eggs. Consequently, it is necessary to vacuum more than once to pick up larvae as they hatch out.[9]

Nicholas Lampkin

Walter Kress tractor-mounted beetle collector

Réal Samson, an organic potato farmer in Farnham, Quebec, has developed a PTO-driven implement consisting of a blower which blows air laterally onto the potato plants to dislodge the adults and larvae. The blower is followed by a flamer (mounted two feet behind the blower) which kills the beetles that have landed in the rows. As the blower does not damage the leaves of the plants, the implement can be used as frequently as needed. Réal uses the implement two or three times per week, depending on beetle pressure.

Tractor-mounted Collector

A tractor-mounted beetle collector has been developed by Walter Kress of Germany. It consists of a front- or rear-mounted set of trays positioned on both sides of the hills. Chains are suspended above the plants; these agitate the plants causing the beetles to fall into the trays. A success rate of 90 % has been reported.

Flaming

A hand-held or tractor-mounted flamer can kill up to 90 % of adults and 35 % of egg masses laid on the underside of upper leaves. One study showed that the flamer was most effective when applied to plants that were 8–15 cm (4–6 in) tall. Flaming should be done on warm, sunny days when beetles are active at the top of the plants. Young potato plants can tolerate losses of 20 % of their leaves and 40 % once they have bloomed whether defoliation is due to beetle damage or flame weeding for weed or pest control. [10] Flaming may result in more tubers; however they might be slightly smaller than those of non-flamed plants. [11]

Delayed Planting & Varietal Choice

Some gardeners delay planting of potatoes until mid- to late June so that there are no potato plants in the area when the beetles emerge from hibernation. While this may be a good strategy for storage potatoes, it does not work for new potatoes, which sell well in early markets. Other farmers plant as soon as the soil warms up so that vigorous growth occurs before the beetles appear. Selecting early maturing varieties can ensure early tuber formation.

Planting a Trap Crop

A trap crop consisting of an early potato (such as Norland) can attract Colorado potato beetles. The crop and pests are destroyed by flaming or turning under. Other members of the Solanaceae family, such as Eggplant, are also suitable trap crops.

Beneficial Insects

Natural enemies of the Colorado potato beetle feed on eggs or larvae and include:

- Ladybeetles *(Coleomegilla maculata)*
- Ground beetles *(Lebia grandis)*
- Lacewings (*Chrysoperla* spp.)
- Daddy longlegs *(Phalangium opilio)*
- Spined soldier bug *(Podisus maculiventris)*
- Two-spotted stinkbug *(Perillus bioculatus)*
- Parasitic wasps (*Trichogramma* spp.)
- Two fly species *(Doryphorophaga doryphorae* and *D. coberrans*).

Releases of spined soldier bugs and parasitic wasps have been successful with reports of up to 50 % of CPB egg masses and 90 % of larvae destroyed through well-timed releases at a rate of 2–5 spined soldier bugs per square metre/yard of crop. [12] One grower in southern Ontario found the release of soldier bugs killed 75 % of the larvae. The cost was $247 per hectare ($100 per acre) and the timing of the release was critical to success.

The parasitic fly *(Tachinidae* spp.*)* is known to parasitize as many as 75 % of second generation larvae in some locations. Parasitic nematodes *(Heterorhabditis species)* can be applied to the soil where they attack larvae as they prepare to pupate.

Marv Dyck applies spinosad to the outer rows of the crop, 16 metres (54 ft) wide on the long sides and 6 metres (20 ft) wide on the ends. In this way, one acre is sprayed out of every forty. By spraying only the perimeter of the field, beneficial insects are provided with a refuge in the centre of the field and continue to help control pests. "Let nature maintain the balance and provide a buffering capacity," says Marv.

Biological Pesticides

If preventive measures fail, biological pesticides such as Spinosad can be used, but they may kill beneficial insect larvae as well as pests. Check with your certifier before using any pest control products to ensure that the active ingredients and the formulants in the product are accepted under the Canadian Organic Standards.

Spinosad is an aerobic fermentation product of *Saccharopolyspora spinosa*, a soil bacterium. Spinosad should be applied at the peak of egg hatching. It kills larvae a few minutes after it has been ingested.

There is concern about the effect of spinosad on aquatic organisms, earthworms and microorganisms. Avoid using spinosad when plants are in bloom as it is toxic to bees. Some growers use spinosad as a perimeter spray to protect beneficial insects.

POTATO LEAFHOPPERS *(Empoasca fabae)*

DESCRIPTION

Potato leafhoppers are wedge-shaped flying insects, about 5 mm (¼ in.) long, and gray, green or brown in colour. Immature nymphs are smaller and wingless. Leafhoppers do not overwinter in most of Canada but are carried by upper level warm winds from the U.S. and can arrive as early as May. Depending on the weather and the region, there can be two to four generations each year. Alfalfa is the preferred host; cutting alfalfa hay fields causes leafhoppers to move to other crops. Potato fields adjacent to alfalfa stands are particularly vulnerable to sudden population spikes. Some species transmit viral diseases, such as aster yellows and witches' broom. The interest in developing "hairy leaf" potato varieties which are repellent to the leafhopper has been stimulated by the absence of other options for potato leafhopper control.

IMPACT

Adults and nymphs feed on potato leaves causing leaf puckering and hopperburn (browning of the leaf margins). Hopperburn is the die-back resulting from a toxin injected by the leafhopper. Hopperburn is sometimes confused with drought stress. To avoid a reduction in yield, leafhoppers must be controlled before hopperburn occurs.

STRATEGIES

Isaiah Swidersky's greatest challenge has been controlling leafhoppers. He has gained the support of his neighbours to maintain a refuge for leafhoppers in their alfalfa fields. His neighbours have agreed to hay their alfalfa fields in two stages. They mow the outside half first and leave the centre as a refuge while the outer half regrows. As leafhoppers prefer tender alfalfa, maintaining a refuge ensures that they will not migrate to the potato crop. Leafhoppers also feed on soybeans.

Offering an Alternative Feed

Alfalfa fields can be managed to keep the leafhopper in the alfalfa, rather than migrate to the potato fields. The key is to maintain an alfalfa refuge for the leafhoppers by cutting part of the field and leaving the rest until the first grows back.

Resistant Varieties

Leafhopper tolerance in 55 varieties of potatoes was studied at Star Flower Farm and Cornell University's Freeville Organic Research Farm.[13] Results showed a wide variation in response to leafhoppers; high resistance was found in King Harry, Chieftain, Katadin, Superior, Green Mountain, Carola, Russet Burbank and Elba. Mid-range tolerance was observed for Yukon Gold, and Island Sunshine landed in the bottom third.

Neem Oil

Neem oil (derived from the leaves and seeds of the *Azadirachta indica* tree) is believed to be effective in controlling leafhoppers; however the commercial product has not received approval from Health Canada's Pest Management Regulatory Agency (PMRA). A kilogram (2.2 lb) of neem leaves (which is available at health food stores) can be combined with two litres (0.5 gal) of water. Allow the leaves to soak overnight and then boil the mixture for 15–20 minutes until it is reduced to one quarter of its original volume. Dilute the extract with water to make four to five litres (1–1.3 gal). A small amount of phosphate-free detergent .3ml (1/16 tsp) or molasses helps the sprayed solution adhere to the leaves of the plant.[14] As neem breaks down in four to five days of sunlight, repeated applications are required.[15]

Pyrethrin

Aside from neem oil, natural source pyrethrin is the only organic pest control product which is effective against potato leafhoppers. Pyrethrins are derived from an extract of chrysanthemum plants. The plant extract is called pyrethrum and contains pyrethrin I and pyrethrin II. The synthetic form is called pyrethroid and is not permitted in organic agriculture. Natural source pyrethrins which are formulated with piperonyl butoxide are also prohibited. Natural source pyrethrins may however be combined with soap to increase adherence to the leaves. Some producers combine pyrethrins with neem oil for added efficacy. As pyrethrins are toxic to bees, they should be applied early in the morning or late evening to avoid times when bees are in the field. For cost effectiveness, pest products should not be applied until leafhopper pressure reaches ten nymphs per hundred leaves.[16]

POTATO APHIDS *(Macrosiphum euphorbiae)*

DESCRIPTION

A number of varieties of aphids feed on potato plants, including the green peach aphid *(Myzus persicae)* and the potato aphid *(Macrosiphum euphorbiae)*. The green peach aphid is almond-shaped, usually yellow and primarily found on lower leaves. The potato aphid is similar in shape and colour but is larger and usually found on the upper leaves. The buckthorn aphid *(Aphis nasturtii)* and the foxglove aphid *(Aulacorthum solani)* appear occasionally in Ontario.

IMPACT

Plants are damaged from the large numbers of aphids feeding and from diseases which they carry such as the Potato Leaf Roll Virus.

STRATEGIES

Practice proper crop rotation. Beneficial insects such as ladybugs and aphid lions are renowned for their predation on aphids. Some farmers have used soap spray and garlic spray with success.

WIREWORMS *(Agriotes lineatus, A.obscures)*

DESCRIPTION

Wireworms are yellowish-brown, shiny, slender, hard-bodied worms. Wireworms are the larval stage of the click beetle. Larvae start to move upward in the soil when soil temperatures reach 10°C (50°F).

IMPACT

Wireworms can be a problem for the first two years following grass sod. Wireworms damage seed pieces and crowns of young plants and then tunnel into tubers. "Losses in [conventional] potato production alone in the Lower Fraser Valley of British Columbia were reported in 1994 between $500,000 and $800,000.[17]

STRATEGIES

Cover Crop

A cover crop of oilradish or mustard has been reported to be effective against wireworms. However, one study showed marginal effectiveness with 36% wireworm damage to potatoes in untreated plots, 32% damage following an oilradish cover crop and 29% wireworm damage in potatoes following a mustard cover crop. [18]

Predicting Wireworm Density

A pheromone trap for click beetles can also be used to gauge the beetle population and is available from www.pherotech.com.

A fairly accurate prediction of wireworm population density can be done by checking for click beetles in the forage crop preceding potatoes in the rotation. Click beetles are flat, brown or black beetles which can be identified by the clicking sound they make when they jump to evade capture. If click beetles are numerous, an intervening cover crop may be planted for control or nematodes can be released to control the wireworm population in the following season.

To assess wireworm density at the beginning of the potato crop year, traps consisting of a piece of potato or carrot can be buried in several holes 10 cm (4 in.) deep around the field. Mark the locations and check in two or three days. If one or two wireworms are found, the danger to the crop is considered high. If four or more wireworms are found in each trap, the risk to potatoes is extremely high and serious damage to the crop is likely.

Trap Tubers

Market gardeners sometimes plant potato tubers as traps adjacent to the potato rows. These are marked with a stake. Before tubers start to form on the potato plants, the trap tubers are pulled up and the wireworms destroyed.

Nematodes & other Biologicals

Steinernema and *Heterorhabditis* nematodes may be applied to the soil once it has warmed up in the spring, but this can be a costly option. Research suggests that the insect fungal pathogen *Metarhizium anisopliae* may be effective as a biological control agent for *Agriotes obscurus.* [19]

WHITE GRUBS *(Phyllophaga* spp.*)*

DESCRIPTION

White grubs are the large white larvae of the June beetle which prefer sod as a habitat.

IMPACT

Two-year old white grubs feed on potatoes and are a problem in potato fields that follow sod. They leave large holes which affect the marketability of the tubers.

STRATEGIES

Rotating potato crops with non-susceptible crops such as oats, rye, clover, orchardgrass or alfalfa eliminates the habitat for the white grub. In a severe infestation early fall and late spring plowing can be effective; plowing kills the grubs as well as brings them to the surface to be eaten by birds.

Milky disease, also known as milky spore disease (*Bacillus papillae* or *B. lentimorbus*), can be applied to control Japanese beetle grubs. It should be applied in the late spring or early fall when soil temperatures are at least 21°C (70°F). It may take several seasons for control to be complete and will not succeed unless grubs are present when the bacteria are applied. *Steinernema* and *Heterorhabditis* nematodes and the fungal organisms, *Beauveria bassiana* and *Metarhizium anisopliae,* are also effective white grub control agents. However, application of nematodes and fungal organisms may not be cost-effective for large fields.

NEMATODES *(Globodera* spp.*)*

DESCRIPTION

Pest nematodes are minute roundworms which enter plants through wounds in the root zone. Once a pest nematode species is established in a field, it is usually impossible to eliminate it completely.

Cyst nematodes include both golden nematodes and pale cyst nematodes. Golden nematodes (*Globodera rostochiensis*) have been identified in isolated fields in Newfoundland, Vancouver Island, Quebec and most recently, in Alberta in 2007. Golden nematodes are the most challenging species as they can reduce potato yields by as much as 80%. Pale cyst nematodes

(*Globodera pallida*) have been found in Newfoundland. Root lesion nematodes (*Pratylenchus penetrans*) are found in sandy soils in PEI and can reduce potato yields by 40%. Northern root knot nematodes (*Meloidognye hapla*) have been found in Atlantic Canada.

Three species are on the Canadian Food Inspection Agency (CFIA) quarantine list[20] and should be reported if found: Potato cyst nematodes (including golden nematode and Pale cyst nematode), Columbia root-knot nematodes and potato rot nematodes.

Nematodes are difficult to identify in the field; problems are often recognized by the nature of the damage to the tubers. The presence of golden nematodes can be detected by golden-yellow cysts on potato roots. Columbia root-knot nematodes cause rough galls on tubers and the potato rot nematode produces dark brown to black lesions, accompanied by deep black fissures on the surface of the tubers.

IMPACT

Damage includes leaf yellowing, lesions and stunted growth or excessive growth, such as root galls, swollen root tips or unnatural root branching.

STRATEGIES

Crop Rotation

Crop rotations that promote biological diversity can prevent the build-up of pest nematodes, including northern root knot nematodes and potato cyst nematodes. Rotating potatoes with non-host crops such as ryegrass, timothy grass or cereal grains can reduce nematode populations. Cover crops are effective only if the nematode population is below a threshold of ten eggs or juveniles per cubic centimetre (.06 cubic inch) of soil.

Some potato growers in Michigan report that two years of alfalfa in the crop rotation limits nematodes in the potato crop, with the side benefit of improved yields due to soil conditioning and nitrogen fixation. Another effective rotation uses winter grain, followed by potatoes, then a summer cover crop of sorghum-sudangrass and followed by another year in grain.[21] A plowdown of a brassica cover crop, such as oilseed radish or mustard, before planting potatoes the following spring can result in a marked reduction in nematode populations. A cover crop of marigold (*Tagetes patula*) can also be effective against nematodes.

Sorghum-sudangrass is becoming common in corn-growing regions of Canada as a late fall pasture crop.

Variety Selection
Some varieties of potatoes can have acceptable yields despite the presence of nematodes. For example, Domino, Atlantic, Belchip, Campbell 13, Cupids, Donna and Hudson can tolerate potato cyst nematodes. Root lesion nematodes will affect the yield of Superior potatoes if the population exceeds 2000 per kg (900 per lb) of soil; Russet Burbank, Kennebec and Shepody can tolerate populations up to 5000 per kg (2200 per lb) of soil.

POTATO FLEA BEETLES *(Epitrix cucumeris)*

DESCRIPTION

Potato flea beetles are small, black, fast-jumping beetles which overwinter in crop stubble and migrate to potato fields in the spring. Their eggs hatch into larvae which feed on root hairs and then pupate after 4–5 weeks. Potato flea beetles prefer to feed on potatoes but will feed on other members of the solanaceae family as well as brassicas such as broccoli, cabbage or kale.

IMPACT

Flea beetles produce a shot-hole appearance to the leaves. Occasionally flea beetles tunnel under the tuber skin producing cracks and pimples that resemble common scab.

STRATEGIES

Flaming the upper leaves in the spring on sunny warm days when the potato plant is less than 15 cm (6 in.) high can reduce populations of potato flea beetles by 80 % with only a slight reduction in potato yield.

TARNISHED PLANT BUG *(Lygus lineolaris)*

DESCRIPTION

Tarnished plant bugs are green to brown, mottled, 0.6 cm (¼-in.) bugs with a black-tipped yellow triangle on the forewings. They overwinter in fencerow debris.

IMPACT

Tarnished plant bugs feed on leaves, stems and petioles leaving large ragged holes. They introduce a toxin which can cause wilt and premature blossom drop. Tarnished plant bugs may spread the Potato Spindle Tuber Viroid.

STRATEGIES

Floating row covers have been used by market gardeners to control tarnished plant bugs. A strategy more appropriate for larger fields might be to attract beneficial insects such as bigeyed bugs (*Geocoris* spp.), damsel bugs (family *Nabidae*) and minute pirate bugs *(Orius tristicolor)* by providing ground cover and pollen sources. Minute pirate bugs are available commercially for release.

Footnotes

1 Salaman, Redcliffe N. 1970. *The History and Social Influence of the Potato.* Cambridge University Press.

2 Hiiesaar, K. et al. 2006. Over-wintering of the Colorado potato beetle (*Leptinotarsa decemlineata Say*) in field conditions and factors affecting its population density in Estonia. *Agronomy Research* 4(1).

3 Neel, Caroline S. 1992. *Alternative Methods for Controlling the Colorado potato beetle.* West Virginia University Centre for Sustainable and Alternative Agriculture. www.wvu.edu/~exten/infores/pubs/pest/altmeth.pdf

4 Boiteau, G., Lynch D.H. & Martin, R.C. 2008. Influence of Fertilization on the Colorado potato beetle, *Leptinotarsa decemlineata* in organic potato production. *Journal of Environmental Entomology*, 37(2).

5 Bernard, Guy. *Organic Potato Production – A Pest Management Perspective Part One: Insect Control.* Organic Agricultural Centre of Canada. www.organicagcentre.ca/NewspaperArticles/na_org_pot_part1.asp

6 Stoner, Kimberly A. 1998, *Alternatives to Insecticides for Managing Vegetable Insects.* (Proceedings of a Farmer/Scientist Conference) Natural Resource, Agriculture, and Engineering Service (NRAES-138). www.nraes.org

7 See 5

8 Cornell University. *Integrated Crop and Pest Management Guidelines: Potatoes.* Cornell University Extension: www.nysaes.cornell.edu/recommends/24frameset.html

9 Lampkin, Nicholas. 2002. *Organic Farming.* Old Pond.

10 See 3

11 See 5

12 See 5

13 Caldwell, Brian. 2004. *Starflower and Freeville Organic Potato Trials.* Cornell University. Available online at www.plbr.cornell.edu/PSI/StarflowerandFreevillePotato04.pdf

14 Panhwar, Farzana. 2004. Controlling pests with plants. *Eco-Farm & Garden,* Spring 2004. Canadian Organic Growers.

15 Ellis, B.W. & Bradley, F.M., eds. 1992. *The Organic Gardener's Handbook of Natural Insect and Disease Control.* Rodale Press.

16 Seaman, Abby. *Potato Leafhopper.* Cornell University IPM Extension Factsheet. nysipm.cornell.edu/vegetables/nofa/default.asp

17 Wheeler, Robin. February, 2004. The Worrisome Lowdown on the Wiley Wireworm. *BC Organic Grower.* www.certifiedorganic.bc.ca

18 Frost David et al. 2002. *Wireworm Control Using Fodder Rape and Mustard – Evaluating the Use of Brassica Green Manures for the Control of Wireworms in Organic Crops.* ADAS. Available at www.orgprints.org

19 See 17

20 CFIA. *Quarantine notifications.* www.inspection.gc.ca/english/plaveg/pestrava/gloros/glorose.shtml

21 Everts, Kathryne L. et al. *Cover Crops Deter Root-Damaging Nematodes in Vegetable Systems.* Conference 2003 Highlights, Sustainable Agriculture Research and Education. www.sare.org/highlights/2003/nematode.htm

Rose Mountain Farm

Isaiah Swidersky, Alliston, Ontario

Cash crops:
potatoes, alfalfa hay

Green manure:
alfalfa

Irrigation:
none. Precipitation: 82 cm (32.4 in.)

Soil:
sandy loam to clay, pH 6.5

Farm size:
35 ha (86 ac) plus rented fields, 26 ha (65 ac) in potatoes

History:
certified organic by OC/Pro since 2004

Maureen Bostock

Isaiah Swidersky

Isaiah Swidersky farms near Alliston, a region in Ontario known for its intensive potato production. Rose Mountain Farm produces certified organic potatoes on 26 ha (65 ac) of land rented from ecologically minded farmers in the neighbourhood. Isaiah notes that the transition and certification of leased land requires landlords who understand the principles of organic agriculture and respect the requirement for buffers between the organic fields and their other fields. Isaiah has recently purchased a 35 ha (86 ac) farm, with 20 ha (50 ac) tillable.

Isaiah's average yield is 11–22 tonnes per hectare (5-10 tons per acre). Nitrogen is supplied by a three-year stand of alfalfa which is plowed down in the fall before potatoes are planted. Additional nutrients are supplied by the application of compost at 11 tonnes per hectare (5 tons per acre) before plowdown. Occasionally Isaiah adds Sul-Po-Mag or lime as needed. His soil ranges from sandy to clay loam, with a pH of 6.5.

Isaiah grows a variety called Atlantic which is shipped from the field for the organic chipping industry. He also grows tablestock varieties – Superior, Kennebec, Estima and Norland – as well as an experimental variety for SunRISE Produce. His tablestock potatoes are sold to an organic distributor and in the local market.

Crop rotation is Isaiah's main strategy for controlling insects, diseases and weeds. After three years in alfalfa and one year in potatoes, he plants spelt in the fall, and then frost seeds red clover. After a year in red clover, the field returns to potatoes. After harvest, the field is seeded to a winter rye cover crop, followed by alfalfa. On lighter soils, Isaiah may follow alfalfa with potatoes, then spelt or rye overseeded with red clover, followed by oats or potatoes. Occasionally, because Isaiah rents fields, there may be only one year between two crops of potatoes, after which the field returns to a perennial stand of alfalfa. He aims to keep the ground covered with a living crop year-round as much as possible.

Early blight has been a problem. Isaiah selects early blight-resistant varieties and uses fish emulsion, molasses and copper foliar spray which have been effective when applied early.

Entrust is a spinosad product by Dow Chemical.

Isaiah's greatest challenge has been controlling leafhoppers. He has gained the support of his neighbours to maintain a refuge for leafhoppers in their alfalfa fields. His neighbours have agreed to hay their alfalfa fields in two stages. They mow the outside half first and leave the centre as a refuge while the outer half regrows. As leafhoppers prefer tender alfalfa, maintaining a refuge ensures that they will not migrate to the potato crop. Leafhoppers also feed on soybeans.

"It is not an exact science," he says. If the leafhoppers become abundant in his fields, Isaiah sprays with Trounce, an insecticidal soap with natural pyrethrins. Trounce has short-term effectiveness against leafhoppers, tarnished plant bugs and aphids.

Regular scouting of the fields allows Isaiah to monitor the development of pest pressure. Colorado potato beetles are not a major threat and are controlled by hand picking while weeding. Entrust is sprayed if beetle pressure becomes heavy. Because Isaiah's fields are dispersed throughout the neighbouring farms, a problem may develop in one field while the others are unaffected.

9 THE CHALLENGE: DISEASES

THE LIST OF DISEASES to which potatoes are susceptible is daunting, but many organic farmers have noticed that their fields are surprisingly free of diseases. The conventional practice of monoculture leads to a build-up of disease and pest pressures, whereas crop rotation offers organic farmers an effective strategy that prevents many disease problems and has many other benefits as well.

Diseases of potatoes are transmitted to the crop through four main vectors:

- seed pieces
- insects
- soil
- wind

Planting certified seed helps to keep diseases from becoming established on the farm. Planting whole seed can eliminate the opportunity for infection of seed pieces. Insect-borne diseases can be difficult to control. Good organic management practices however, can reduce insect pressure. Wind-borne diseases such as late blight can also be challenging but strategies can be used to reduce the incidence and severity of the disease. Planting potato varieties with resistance to major diseases can be helpful.

RESISTANCE TO MAJOR DISEASES

(M) denotes moderate resistance; all other varieties in the table have high resistance.

RESISTANCE TO:	VARIETIES
Leaf late blight	French Fingerlings (M), Kennebec (M), Onaway (M), Atlantic (M), Island Sunshine
Tuber late blight	Desiree, Chieftain (M), Estima (M), Hertha (M), Penta (M), Agria (M)
Early blight	Kennebec (M)

RESISTANCE TO:	VARIETIES
Common scab	Chieftain (M), Norland, Viking (M), Banana, Estima (M), French Fingerlings (M), Penta (M), Goldrush, Kennebec (M), Onaway (M), Superior (M), Island Sunshine, Eramosa (M) Norkotah Russet
Verticillium wilt	Chieftain (M), Atlantic (M), Cascade
Potato leaf roll virus	Hertha (M), Yukon Gold, Fianna (M), Eramosa
Rhizoctonia / scurf	Desiree, Chieftain (M), Eramosa
Hollow heart	Norland, Desiree, Sieglinde, Goldrush, Norkotah Russet

Hollow Heart is a common disorder which can result from high soil moisture and/or rapid growth.

SUSCEPTIBILITY TO MAJOR DISEASES

(M) denotes moderate susceptibility; all other varieties in the table have high susceptibility.

SUSCEPTIBLE TO:	VARIETIES
Leaf late blight	Desiree (M), Norland, Viking, Banana, Estima (M), Hertha (M), Penta (M), Sieglinde, Yukon Gold, Fianna, Goldrush, Superior, Warba, White Rose, Agria (M)
Tuber late blight	Fianna (M), Kennebec
Early blight	Atlantic, Goldrush, Cascade (M), Onaway, Norkotah Russet, Yukon Gold
Common scab	Desiree, Hertha (M), Yukon Gold, Fianna (M), Kennebec, Warba, White Rose, Agria (M), Russian Blue, All Blue
Verticillium wilt	Norland. Banana (M), Kennebec, Onaway, Superior, Warba, White Rose
Potato leaf roll virus	Viking, Penta (M), Sieglinde, Desiree (M), Chieftain, Norland, Banana, Estima (M), Kennebec, Superior, Warba, White Rose
Rhizoctonia	Yukon Gold, Warba
Hollow heart	Yukon Gold, Atlantic

EARLY BLIGHT *(Alternaria solani)*

DESCRIPTION

Early blight is a common fungal disease that is more severe when the crop is under stress. Symptoms include dark brown to black spots on the leaves with concentric rings, surrounded by a narrow-yellowish border, irregular in shape and up to 1 cm (0.4 in.) in diameter. Spots develop first on older leaves spreading to younger leaves. Early blight occurs most often in cool (17–24°C / 63–75°F), humid weather conditions. The infection can occur at harvest as the blight becomes established in cuts, bruises and wounds in the tubers. Infected tubers develop dark brown to black slightly sunken external lesions which may appear after several months of storage.

Early blight is present in most soils where potatoes have been grown, as the bacteria overwinters on decaying plant material. [1]Plants are most susceptible when they are stressed by drought, insect damage, air pollution or even rapid growth when the tubers are sizing up. As well, plants infected with Verticillium Wilt or that show common mosaic symptoms are susceptible to early blight. [2]

STRATEGIES

Crop health and sanitation in the field are critical to control the spread of early blight:

- Ensure adequate soil fertility for a vigorous crop that can resist the impact of disease organisms
- Control weeds to prevent crowding
- Use a crop rotation to prevent the build-up of soilborne disease
- Turn under crop residue promptly after harvest
- Plant a cover crop as soon after harvest as possible

LATE BLIGHT *(Phytophthora infestans)*

DESCRIPTION

High moisture and cool conditions favour the development of this fungal disease. Late blight overwinters in infected cull tubers or seed tubers and develops initially inside the stems and new foliage from infected seed pieces. Temperatures of 12–20°C (53–68°F) and a few hours of rain encourage the formation of spores which are spread by the wind.

Symptoms develop in four to six days after infection. Initial symptoms are small light-to-dark green, circular to irregularly-shaped water-soaked spots. Later lesions become grey to tan and are surrounded by a light green halo. The white and fuzzy mycelium of the fungus develops at the edge of the lesions, usually on the underside of the leaf. Entire leaves become blighted and the disease can spread to the whole field in a few days.

Tuber infection occurs when water carries the spores onto the tuber in the hill. Tubers can also become infected if harvested while vines have active lesions. External symptoms of tuber infection include irregularly shaped, slightly sunken areas of brown to purple discolouration. A reddish-brown granular dry rot develops in the tuber. Secondary bacteria often take hold. Bacterial soft rot, which is slimy and foul-smelling, develops rapidly in infected tubers under warm, humid field or storage conditions.

STRATEGIES

Prevention

- Plant early maturing or resistant varieties. Kennebec, Elba, Onaway, Rosa, Sebago and Island Sunshine show varying rates of resistance[3].
- Plant rows in line with prevailing winds to deter late blight from moving across the rows and spreading the infection.
- Keep weeds down in the row to provide more air circulation, and avoid irrigating late in the season. High humidity in the field can increase susceptibility of potato plants to late blight.
- Scout fields twice a week during the latter part of the season, in particular the low areas of the fields. Disk in any diseased plants to prevent the spread to healthy plants. If plants are removed from the field, they should be bagged to prevent dispersal of spores.
- If late blight is found in the potato field, a delay of two weeks between top-kill and harvest can reduce the migration of the late blight fungus to the tubers.
- Once the potatoes are in storage, maintain optimum storage temperature and humidity to control disease development. Discard diseased tubers. As late blight overwinters on seed tubers, cull potatoes or tubers left in the field, it is important to ensure that all cull potatoes are collected, piled and properly buried, composted or fed to livestock.

Compost Tea

Compost tea applications have other benefits in addition to disease control. In one study, the application of compost tea as a supplemental source of nutrients resulted in an increase in marketable yields of potatoes, up to almost 20 % higher than untreated potatoes and 15 % higher than plots given nutrients in other forms. Potatoes sprayed with compost tea had more nutrients, such as iron (1700 %), boron, potassium and magnesium, than those plants which did not receive tea.[8]

The microorganisms in compost tea are thought to displace fungal spores on the surface of the leaf. While some studies suggest that non-aerated teas perform better than aerated when used in an anti-fungal application, compost tea trials in Europe[4] and Canada[5] have been unable to confirm the capability of aerated and non-aerated compost teas to control late blight in the field.

A number of variables may affect the efficacy of compost tea, including:

- competition from unwanted organisms
- exposure to UV radiation (which affects compost tea organisms)
- variability in raw materials used to make the tea
- the production process, including the cleanliness of the tank
- application methods and timing (including weather conditions)
- pathogen pressure

Control of late blight requires that the compost microbes remain active for an extended period. Sustaining the activity of bacteria on the leaf surface may be difficult because the environment of a leaf is quite different from the natural habitat of compost microorganisms (soil).

Full strength compost tea can be sprayed on the crop at a rate of 654 litres per hectare (70 gal/acre) as many as ten times over the course of the growing season, starting when the plants are 15 cm (6 in.) tall. A non-aerated formula could be one part compost in five parts water soaked in a burlap sack for a week or so. High volume boom sprays and air-assist sprayers are most effective in providing complete coverage of foliage and stems.[6]

Compost tea has come under scrutiny in recent years due to the concern that improper preparation may result in *E. coli* contamination.[7]

Contamination can be prevented by following these practices:

- Use only high quality potable water
- Clean brewing equipment thoroughly
- Use only fully composted materials, which have undergone a thermophilic phase
- Keep brewing equipment covered to prevent contamination by birds, animals or insects
- Avoid the use of additives (e.g. molasses)

Compost tea which is made with additives should not be used in a late blight prevention program because of the risk of contamination by *E. coli.* If additives are used, the compost tea should be applied more than 120 days before harvesting crops which are in contact with the soil, as a supplemental source of nutrients for the crop. Compost teas containing additives can be batch tested and if the sample batch is found to be free of *E. coli*, any additional batches produced in the same manner can be used without restriction.

Other Foliar Sprays

Foliar applications of kelp and the biodynamic preparation no. 508, an extract of horsetail (*Equisetum arvense*), are thought to be effective against late blight. Extracts of lemon verbena (*Lippia adoensis*) and peppercress (*Lepidium sativum*) have also been mentioned as possible treatments. More field study of botanical extracts is needed.

Copper

Copper sprays are permitted under the Canadian Organic Standards provided excessive copper does not build up in the soil. Copper sprays such as Bordeaux Mix are effective against late blight; however, to be effective, the copper solution has to be on the leaf surface before blight appears and must be applied more than once during the season.

VERTICILLIUM WILT *(Verticillium dahliae)*

DESCRIPTION

For more information, see Chapter 8 (The Challenges: Pests) under Nematodes

Verticillium wilt is a fungal disease which has a wide range of hosts and is very persistent in the soil. The first indication of infection is the yellowing of lower leaves, spreading later to upper leaves. Insect damage, heat and drought increase the severity of verticillium wilt. In combination with nematodes, a severe infection of verticillium wilt can cause premature die-back which results in significantly lower yields of small tubers.

STRATEGIES

Use long-term rotations with non-nematode hosting crops such as cereals, ryegrass, timothy or alfalfa.

SCAB *(Streptomyces scabies, S. acidiscabies)*

DESCRIPTION

Common scab is a bacterium that persists in the soil and causes lesions on the skins of potato tubers. The lesions range from moderate to severe depending on variety resistance and environmental conditions. Potatoes can be rendered unmarketable by severe lesions. Some varieties, such as Superior, Cherokee, Onaway and Norland, are moderately resistant to common scab. Warm, dry soils which coincide with tuber maturation are conducive to the development of scab. Soil pH is also a factor. Scab prefers a soil pH of 6.0-7.5; acid-tolerant *Streptomyces acidiscabies* however, can survive in soils with a pH as low as 5.0.

Powdery scab (*Spongospora subterranea*) is a fungal disease which produces many small growths on the surface of tubers and is often mistaken for common scab. Powdery scab is not found in many parts of Canada but can be a problem in Northern Ontario. Heavy clay soils combined with wet conditions favour the development of powdery scab. Powdery scab can cause dry rot in storage and can spread to other potatoes.

STRATEGIES

Avoid heavy applications of limestone. If irrigation is used, maintain high soil moisture for about four weeks after tuber set. Recent research has shown that the application of compost reduces the incidence of scab: the compost microorganisms displace scab-producing organisms in the soil. Plant early-generation, disease-free, resistant varieties of potato seed in warm, well drained soil. Do not plant in fields in which scab has occurred in the last four years. Clean potato seed and long rotations are the key to preventing powdery scab.

RHIZOCTONIA / SCURF *(Rhizoctonia solani)*

DESCRIPTION

Symptoms of rhizoctonia, often called black scurf, include stem and stolon cankers, aerial tubers, leaf rolling, premature death of plants and tuber malformations. Black scurf on infected tuber surfaces can reduce marketability. Rhizoctonia is a seed- and soil-borne fungus and occurs more frequently during cool, wet springs.

STRATEGIES

Crop rotation prevents the build-up of rhizoctonia, as does the use of clean certified seed. Research from New Brunswick suggests that lobster and crab shell waste can reduce rhizoctonia as well as provide plant nutrition. A substance in lobster shells encourages soil bacteria to make chitinase which breaks down the cell walls of fungal pathogens such as rhizoctonia.[9]

SILVER SCURF *(Helminthosporium solani)*

DESCRIPTION

Silver scurf is a fungal infection which causes unsightly brown blemishes on the surface of the tuber, thereby reducing marketability. As the blemishes develop, they become silvery in appearance. The fungus causes the outer layer of the tuber's skin to slough off. Tubers lose moisture and shrink in storage. The infected tuber has a greater susceptibility to other diseases. Infected seed potatoes are noted to have reduced vigour.

STRATEGIES

As Silver scurf is transmitted primarily from infected seed potatoes, using disease-free potato seed is very important. Infected volunteers left in the field can infect the succeeding crop. A four year interval in the rotation between potato crops protects tubers from volunteer-transmitted diseases.

TUBER ROT IN THE FIELD AND IN STORAGE

General preventive practices can protect against a number of organisms which produce rot during the growing season or in storage.

- Fusarium dry rot *(Fusarium* spp.*)* occurs as dry rot and seed piece decay in storage and sometimes after the seed-piece has been planted. Delay planting until the soil warms up. Crop rotation can prevent fusarium from building up in the soil.
- Bacterial soft rot (*Erwinia carotovora* subsp. *carotovora)* produces a slimy, foul-smelling decay of tubers and often sets in when soil temperatures are high. Weedy conditions are optimal for the development of bacterial soft rot. The bacteria can also be transmitted through infected seed.

- Black leg (*Erwinia carotovora* subsp. *atroseptica*), sometimes called crown rot, is a common bacterial disease characterized by black rot at the stem end. This disease is associated with cool, wet soils, poor sanitation and seed cutting hygiene. Use whole seed if possible.
- Leak (*Pythium ultimum* var. *ultimum*) is a fungal disease which enters immature potatoes that have been harvested under warm conditions. Symptoms include cream to black watery rot with water dripping from the diseased tubers. Avoid injuring delicate new potatoes. If harvesting during warm weather, immediately cool the tubers and ensure good air movement in storage.

VIRUSES AND QUARANTINE DISEASES

VIRUSES

Viruses can reduce crop yield and tuber quality. Symptoms generally include mosaic patterning on leaves, stunting of plants, leaf malformation and tuber malformations. Plants and tubers sometimes show no symptoms, depending on soil fertility, weather and the age of the plant.

Some potato viruses are transmitted through contaminated seed potatoes. Potato Virus X (PVX), Potato Mop Top Virus (PMTV) and Potato Spindle Tuber Viroid (PSTV) can be controlled by the use of virus-free potato seed. Equipment sanitation is important to prevent the transmission of viruses from infected tubers to healthy ones.

Other viruses such as the Potato Leaf Roll Virus (PLRV), the Alfalfa Mosaic Virus (AMV) and the Potato Virus Y (PVY) are transmitted to the potato plants by aphids. Aphids can be controlled through crop rotation and through the release of beneficial insects such as ladybeetles. PLRV-resistant varieties include Yukon Gold, Hertha, Eramosa and Fianna.

Roguing out plants that show mosaic patterning on the leaves can prevent the increase of viruses. Proper crop rotation avoids the build-up of viruses, some of which can persist in the soil for many years. Mulching has been demonstrated as an effective strategy for preventing the transmission of diseases between soil and plants. The incidence of Potato Virus Y has been found to be lower in mulched potatoes than in bare fields. [10]

QUARANTINE DISEASES

The Canadian Food Inspection Agency monitors the Canadian seed potato supply for organisms that have the potential to devastate potato crops in Canada. They include bacterial ring rot, potato wart fungus, brown rot bacterium (race 3, biovar 2), PVY ^{n} and PVY $^{ntn.}$ Some of these diseases are transmitted by green peach aphids or Colorado potato beetles, and others overwinter in tubers or remain in the soil for decades. Positive identification of these diseases is determined by laboratory tissue testing.

FOOTNOTES

1 Banks, Dr. Eugenia. 2004. *Potato Field Guide: Insects, Diseases and Defects.* OMAFRA publication no. 823

2 Shinners-Carnelley, Tracy et al. *Commercial Potato Production & Disease Management.* Manitoba Agriculture, Food & Rural Initiatives. www.gov.mb.ca/agriculture/crops/potatoes/bda04s07(3-4).htmlno. Bacterial_Diseases

3 Kuepper, George & Sullivan, Preston. 2004. *Organic Alternatives for Late Blight Control in Potatoes.* ATTRA. www.attra.org

4 Leifert, Dr. Carlo. 2004. *Novel Strategies for Control of Fungal Crop Disease.* OACC Potato Symposium. www.organicagcentre.ca/Potato%20Symposium/index.html

5 Sturz, A.V. et al. 2006. Influence of compost tea, powdered kelp and Manzate 75 on bacterial-community composition, and antibiosis against *Phytophthora infestans* in the potato phylloplane. *Canadian Journal of Plant Pathology* 28

6 See 3

7 Sideman, Eric et al. 2004. *Compost Tea Task Force Report.* National Organic Standards Board. www.ams.usda.gov/AMSv1.0/getfile?dDocName=STELPRDC5058470

8 Sayre, Laura. 2003. *Compost Tea Research Enters Its 2nd Year.* Rodale Institute. www.newfarm.org

9 Peters, Rick. 2004. *Seafood Processing Waste for Nutrition & Disease Control in Organically Grown Potatoes.* OACC Potato Symposium. www.organicagcentre.ca/Potato%20Symposium/index.html

10 Doring, Thomas & Sauke, Helmut. 2003. *Straw Mulch and Chitting for Virus Vector Control in Organic Potatoes.* Organic E-prints. www.orgprints.org

Kentdale Farm

Fred Dollar, Winslow, PEI

Cash crops:
hay, wheat, vegetables and potatoes

Green manure:
red clover

Irrigation:
none

Soil:
heavy clay/loam

Farm size:
162 ha (400 ac), 22 ha (55 ac) in potatoes

History:
certified organic by OC/Pro since 2001

Fred Dollar farms 162 hectares (400 ac) on Prince Edward Island with 22 ha (55 ac) in certified organic potatoes and the rest in milling wheat (or oats) and forages. The farm became certified organic in 2001 after Fred realized that there were no local organic potato farmers ready to serve the growing market.

Today, Fred sells tablestock to markets in Atlantic Canada and the eastern seaboard of the United States. His preferred varieties are Red Norland, Kennebec and Goldrush – a russet baking variety which performs well under organic growing conditions. He also produces certified organic certified potato seed.

Unlike many farms in PEI which have sandy soils, Fred farms on heavy clay/loam, yielding 24-33 tonnes/ha (225–300 cwt or 11-15 tons per acre) depending on the variety. The moisture retention and fertile clay soils, combined with his soil-building program, help Fred produce a top quality organic potato which resists disease and insects.

Fred uses a four-year rotation. In the first year, wheat is grown, underseeded to red clover followed in the second year by potatoes, then wheat underseeded and in the final year, the field is seeded out to hay. Manure is applied the fall before planting potatoes. Sulfate of potash (75%) and Sul-po-mag (25%) is applied at the rate of 112 kg per hectare (100 lb per acre) on the wheat crop and 560 kg per hectare (500 lb per acre) on the potatoes in the spring. Lime is applied regularly to keep the pH in the 6+ range. Liquid seaweed is applied at the rate of 1.85 litres per

Fred cautions new farmers wanting to get into organic potatoes that the market for organic potatoes is small. As more and more conventional potato producers tap into the organic market, the price premium may continue to shrink. Fred notes that people who buy organic food are not as concerned with the price as with the quality. "Anyone who has tasted a sweet organic potato knows how it compares against the bitter taste of conventional stock."

hectare (0.2 gallons to the acre) four or five times during the growing season. Seaweed is combined with copper to combat late blight if needed. Irrigation is not required as PEI's coastal climate supplies adequate rainfall.

Late blight is a serious problem on the Island with significant losses most years. It has been four years since Fred's crop had a major infection; at that time, he lost twenty acres of potatoes. Fred attributes his recent success to the use of copper and the rotation of his crops. Fred maintains that organic farming promotes healthy soil and healthy plants.

Colorado potato beetles are not a significant problem. When a field comes under attack, Fred sprays with Entrust. He has noted that only certain fields have a problem with the beetles and believes that healthier plants (whose leaves have a higher sugar content) are less appealing to the beetles. Wireworms are becoming a problem in PEI and Fred hopes that his rotation will protect him from a serious infestation. Wild mustard has become a problem weed in recent years and Fred is planning to purchase a flame weeder to use for weed control and top-kill (this will also help prevent late blight). Fred attributes the absence of disease in his 279 square-metre (3000 sq ft) storage facility to climate control measures which maintain appropriate levels of humidity, temperature and air circulation.

10 Harvesting & Storage

Top-kill

Bruce Miller in the Pemberton Valley of British Columbia uses a vine beater to take the tops off and follows with a six-foot wide flame weeder. By flaming the tops, he reduces the density of disease organisms on the surface of the soil which could otherwise infect tubers during harvest.

Once the potato tubers have reached an optimum number and size, killing the top growth stimulates the skins to harden early. A common method is to mow the plants with a bush hog set high enough to avoid clipping tubers close to the surface. Mature potatoes intended for storage require two weeks between plant death and harvest to ensure the tubers' skins have hardened. Top-kill has the added benefit of discouraging late blight spores from proliferating on decaying plant material or from migrating through the soil and infecting the tubers. British potato producers are experimenting with infrared flamers which kill late blight spores on the ground.

Some growers select a top-kill date at which they begin harvest. That way, harvest can be timed for completion before wet fall weather and to avoid the late blight season. This strategy also prevents the over-sizing of tubers, reducing the risk of hollow heart.

Harvesting

Bruises from rough handling expose the tubers to disease in storage. Bruising increases when the air/soil temperature is below 9°C (48°F).[1] To prevent bruising, avoid dropping potatoes more than 15 cm (6 in.) and pad hard surfaces in the hopper and conveyor.

Keep in mind that new potatoes have very thin skins and a high moisture content; they are extremely vulnerable to injury during harvesting and short-term storage.

Organic producers need to clean equipment and bins which were used previously for conventional potatoes. If custom harvesting equipment and trucks are used, the Canadian Organic Standards require records to include clean-out affidavits to verify that equipment has not been contaminated with conventional residues.

STORAGE

Many producers of organic chipping potatoes use varieties which can be sold to processors out of the field and thus avoid the cost of a storage facility. Producers of organic seed and table stock may require winter storage facilities to be able to sell year round. Storage facilities require attention to temperature, humidity and light control. The Canadian Organic Standards require organic products to be stored separately from conventional products. Organic integrity must be maintained all the way from the seed potato to the market.

Cuts and bruises heal most quickly at temperatures between 15 and 21°C (59-70°F). This temperature range should be maintained for two to three weeks after harvest, and then lowered to 5°C (41°F) for the remainder of the storage period. At 5°C (41°F), most potatoes will remain dormant for eight months. Fluctuations in temperature can shorten dormancy.

Potatoes intended for processing should be maintained at 10°C (50°F) for short storage periods and should not be subjected to temperatures below 5°C (41°F). If processing potatoes are stored at 10°C (50°F) for an extended period of time, they will sprout.

If potatoes are exposed to temperatures between 0°C and 3°C (32-37 °F), discolouration may result. Below 0°C (32°F), ice crystals form and the tissues become soft and watery after thawing. Shepody, a popular chipping potato, is unique among modern commercial varieties because it must be stored at 2°C (35°F) to prevent sprouting.

Brenda Frick

Donna Kislyk loading bins of potatoes into winter storage

The relative humidity in storage should be maintained at 90–95%. Higher levels result in condensation of moisture on tubers and on the storage walls. If the tubers were wet when harvested, the humidity should be kept lower until the skins of the tubers have dried.

The Canadian Organic Standards do not permit the use of chlorpropham on organic potatoes to inhibit sprouting in storage. Researchers have been investigating the use of natural essential oils for sprout inhibition and have had mixed success with clove oil, peppermint oil, spearmint oil, garlic oil, cassia and cinnamon bark compounds (cinnameldehyde). Significant suppression was achieved by diallyl disulphide (extracted from onions) and carvone (found in caraway and dill seeds), but both compounds caused unacceptable off-flavours; however, they could be used in seed potato storage where flavour is not an issue. Garlic powder, peppermint oil and ground cloves were not as effective at suppressing sprouting but had a less negative impact on the flavour of the cooked potatoes.[2]

CULL PILES

Cull piles can be sources of disease on the farm. In Saskatchewan, cull potatoes must be disposed of before June 15th of each year as part of a late blight prevention program. Potatoes culled because of disease, bruising or greening can be buried under 46 cm (18 in.) of soil to promote breakdown and prevent volunteer growth. Any potatoes which sprout in the cull pile should be turned under. Black plastic covering the cull pile increases the rate of decomposition. Follow the same rules for locating a cull pile as for a compost pile, to ensure that run-off from the pile does not pollute waterways.

Cull potatoes can be composted to use as a soil amendment. The carbon/nitrogen ratio must be corrected by adding carbon-rich feedstocks at a rate of two parts straw to one part potatoes. Three parts sawdust can be combined with three parts potatoes and one part solid manure. Besides balancing the carbon/nitrogen ratio, adding carbon reduces the moisture level from 80% to 40–60% which is necessary for aerobic composting. To kill late blight spores, the compost pile must reach a temperature of 45°C (113°F). Air should be introduced by turning the pile. This ensures that the decomposition does not become anaerobic and that decomposition is consistent throughout the pile.

If composting is not an option, the culls can be spread on fields that will not be seeded to potatoes for three to four years and disked under, then followed with a cover crop. This prevents volunteers from sprouting – which could become a source of disease or a habitat for pests – and makes use of the potatoes as an excellent source of fertility.

Cull potatoes are an excellent livestock feed. In the feed ration for mature cattle, two kilograms (4.4 lb) of potatoes can replace 0.5 kg (1 lb) of barley, providing energy in the form of starch. Since the protein content is low, the ration should continue to include high protein feeds and forages to encourage weight gain or milk production. Beef cattle should have no more than 50 % of their protein from potatoes while dairy cows should have no more than 20–25 % of their protein source replaced by potatoes. Giving ruminants a large daily intake of potatoes in the diet should be avoided because it can result in high acid levels in the rumen (although sodium bicarbonate can be added to the diet as a buffer.) Forages should make up the bulk of a ruminant's diet.

With cattle, potatoes are best introduced to the feed ration gradually, no more than 0.9–1.3 kg (2–3 lb) per day until the maximum percentage of the ration is reached:

- Dairy cattle under 300 kg (660 lb): 2 kg / 100 kg of body weight (2 lb / 100 lb)
- Dairy cattle over 300 kg (660 lb): 3 kg / 100 kg of body weight (3 lb / 100 lb)
- Beef cattle over 300 kg (660 lb): 4–5 kg / 100 kg of body weight (4–5 lb / 100 lb)

To prevent choking, cut potatoes should be fed on the ground for cattle to pick up or ground up as part as a mixed ration. Green potatoes should be discarded as they contain glycoalkaloids which are toxic if fed in quantity.

As pigs have difficulty digesting starch, potatoes should be cooked. The feed ration should include high protein feedstuffs such as beans and wheat middlings. If the pigs are fed potatoes with corn, barley or rye, skim milk or oilseed meal should be added.

While raw feeding is the most economical, potatoes can be converted into silage at the rate of 3 parts chopped potatoes to 1 part chopped hay, reducing the moisture content to 60 %. Corn or sorghum-sudangrass can be ensiled at the rate of 4 parts corn or sorghum-sudangrass to 1 part potatoes.

FOOTNOTES

1 Atlantic Potato Committee. *Atlantic Canada Potato Guide.* www.gov.pe.ca/af/agweb/

2 Elsadr, H. & Waterer, D. 2005. *Efficacy of Natural Compounds to Suppress Sprouting and Fusarium Dry Rot in Potatoes.* University of Saskatchewan. www.usask.ca/agriculture/plantssci/vegetable

August Organics

Dan and Christine Vriend, Leduc, Alberta

Cash crops:
vegetables and potatoes

Green manure:
rye and oats

Irrigation:
drip irrigation (average precipitation: 432 mm (17 in.)

Soil:
sandy loam, pH 7.1

Farm size:
40 ha (100 ac), 2 ha (5 ac) in potatoes

History:
certified organic by OPAM since 2004

Dan and Christine Vriend follow in the tradition of Dan's family who were pioneers in the certified organic movement in Alberta. Certified organic since 2004, they farm 40 ha (100 ac) just outside of Leduc, Alberta. Eight hectares (20 ac) are planted to vegetable crops, of which 2 ha (5 ac) are in seed and table potatoes.

The Vriends are the only certified organic certified seed producers in Alberta. They market their vegetables mostly at the Old Strathcona Farmers' Market in Edmonton which operates year round and sell seed potatoes to customers from as far away as the Yukon. Potato varieties include Yukon Gold, Russet Norkotah, All Blue, Bananas, Warba, Eramosa, Rote Erstling and Island Sunshine. Yields are 26-33 tonnes per hectare (12–15 tons/ ac).

Dan's primary strategy is to keep 8 hectares (20 ac) in cover crops, with an equivalent area in vegetables. He uses a 50/50 mix of rye and oats which are turned under in late summer or early fall. He also rotates the crops so that light feeders are followed by heavier feeders. Compost is made from field wastes and applied to heavy feeders such as sweet corn and members of the cabbage family.

Dan plants his potato rows as

Dan's advice to new growers is to sell more than one variety of potatoes on the market stand. "Variety is the key to selling the crop," he says, "If you have one variety on the table it won't sell as well as if you have four." He also notes that eight out of ten new growers will quit after the first year. One will make it to the fifth year and that grower will succeed. Dan believes that it takes five years for the earth to heal itself and for yields to develop. He has found that even in a bad year when some vegetables fail due to hail storms or other problems, his yields have stayed within one tonne (2000 lb) of the previous year.

Dan suggests that new growers talk to other local organic growers. "There is a reason," he says, "why everybody does things a little differently, having adapted to the local climate and soils."

close together as possible so that the canopy chokes out the weeds. He hills the potatoes three times in the season. As soon as the potatoes emerge, he drags a chain over them, knocking the planting hill down. A week later he rebuilds the hill and continues adding to the hill until the canopy closes over. This aggressive approach delays the harvest by 5–10 days, but the increase in yield makes up for it.

Northern Alberta has harsh winters which kill most pests. The summers are long and good for beneficial insects. Dan once experienced the astounding sight of native ladybugs moving by the thousands from the tree line into the crops early in the season.

In 2004, a grasshopper infestation devastated the conventional crops in the area; some lost as much as 30–60%. However the Vriends' crops were virtually untouched. Dan thinks that the ammonia in conventional potato fertilizers inhibits sugar in the conventional plants leaving them susceptible to pest pressure.

Dan's strategy for dealing with the Colorado potato beetles is to drive the tractor with a 3-point hitch tool bar down the rows of plants, knocking the beetles off the plants. He does this twice a day for three days, shortly after the adults emerge from hibernation. The beetles become exhausted and stop feeding.

11 MARKETING ORGANIC POTATOES

"There are examples of people who have gone into organic potatoes in a big way, did not do adequate market research – and crashed and burned."

Isaiah Swidersky

IN 2006, CANADA had 3,555 certified organic farms[1] with more than 539,010 hectares (1,331,875 acres) under cultivation. Organic potatoes were grown on at least 497 hectares (1,228 acres). As the demand for organic products grows by 15–20 % yearly[2], new opportunities to sell organic potatoes are developing, including markets for table stock, gourmet potatoes, chipping potatoes, and processing varieties for soups and frozen foods. To meet future market goals, production should double by 2011 and organic potato acreage should increase to 7,217 hectares (17,833 acres) by 2016.[3]

Even so, organic potato farmers should proceed cautiously. A gradual increase in the organic potato supply will not tip the market beyond what it can absorb, but a sudden surge could result in the collapse of the organic premium. Starting small and gradually increasing acreage of this valuable field crop can offset the risk. Matching supply and demand is an ongoing issue in agriculture and will likely become more critical for organic farmers as organic production approaches the demand threshold over the next few years.

In the past, the market for potatoes was mostly limited to wholesale trade. Today however, new local market opportunities are emerging as urban and rural consumers organize to rebuild the local food economy. Because they understand how globalization has dismantled local food systems, consumers are willing to pay higher prices to support local growers of fresh, healthy organic produce. New retail stores specializing in local organic foods are opening in many rural and urban communities, and farmers in many parts of the country are building co-operative enterprises to keep the shelves stocked year-round. Organic potato farmers are uniquely positioned to participate in these initiatives because potatoes can be sold fresh through the summer and autumn, or out of storage during the winter.

Consumers are beginning to recognize that local organic farming should be supported because it produces high quality food while benefiting the environment through reduced carbon emissions and a smaller ecological footprint.

It takes more than a handful of new farmers markets to create a healthy rural economy, but each step forward counts immeasurably towards securing the future of farming in Canada.

Laura Berman Green Fuse

FOOTNOTES

1 Macey, Anne. 2008. *Certified Organic Production in Canada.* Canadian Organic Growers. (annual statistics available at www.cog.ca)

2 MacRae, Rod et al. 2006. *Ontario Goes Organic: How to Access Canada's Growing Billion Dollar Market For Organic Food.* World Wildlife Fund Canada & Organic Agriculture Centre of Canada. www.organicagcentre.ca/ResearchDatabase/res_oos_intro.asp

3 See 2

RESOURCES

1 INTRODUCTION

Banks, Dr. Eugenia, ed. 2004. *Potato Field Guide: Insects, Diseases and Defects.* Ontario Ministry of Agriculture, Food and Rural Affairs (OMAFRA publication no. 823). An excellent field identification guide with a discussion of internal and external defects of potatoes and many photos of insects and disease symptoms.

Canadian Food Inspection Agency Potato Database. A complete listing of varieties of potatoes registered for commercial use in Canada can be found on the Canadian Food Inspection Agency website, www.inspection.gc.ca

MacRae, Rod et al. 2006. *Ontario Goes Organic: How to Access Canada's Growing Billion Dollar Market For Organic Food.* World Wildlife Fund Canada & Organic Agriculture Centre of Canada.

Wallace, Janet, ed. 2001. *Organic Field Crops Handbook.* Canadian Organic Growers. A comprehensive overview of the principles of organic farming, with particular attention paid to soil science and nutrients in organic farming.

---

2 ORGANIC FARMING

Dwwyor, Llizabet et al, ed. 2005. *Gaining Ground: Making a successful transition to organic farming.* Canadian Organic Growers. This handbook is designed to help transitioning farmers adapt to organic production and focuses on planning, certification, record-keeping, economics and marketing.

Certification agencies in Canada are listed on the Canadian Organic Growers website at www.cog.ca

The Canadian Organic Standards can be downloaded from the website of the Canadian General Standards Board at www.pwgsc.gc.ca/cgsb/on_the_net/organic/index-e.html

The Canadian Organic Office of the Canadian Food Inspection Agency is responsible for enforcing the Canadian Organic Regulation. Regulatory information is available online at www.inspection.gc.ca/english/fssa/orgbio/orgbioe.shtml

Canadian Organic Growers answers frequently-asked questions and provides Standards information on its website www.cog.ca

3 Variety selection & potato breding

Alberta Agriculture and Food. *Botany of the Potato Plant.* www1.agric.gov.ab.ca/$department/deptdocs.nsf/all/opp9546

Duclos, R. & Iarocci, A. The Potato Speaks For Itself. *Seeds of Diversity Journal,* vol.20 no.3, www.seeds.ca

Food and Agriculture Organization (FAO) of the United Nations Year of the Potato, 2008. www.potato2008.org

Ganga, Z. N. & VanderZaag, P.2007. Breeding and Selection for potato varieties that are insect resistant, utilizing trichome-mediated host plant resistance; and have durable resistance to common scab (*Streptomyces spp.*). Project 8928 Final Report. Unpublished.

International Potato Centre (Lima, Peru) research database www.cipotato.org.

Leifert, Dr. Carlo. *Novel Strategies for Control of Fungal Crop Diseases.* www.organicagcentre.ca

Potato Research Centre: to subscribe to the Potato Gene Resources Newsletter or obtain heritage samples, contact the Potato Gene Resources Repository, Potato Research Centre PO Box 20280, Fredericton, NB E3B 4Z7 or phone 506-452-3260.

Ragsdale, D. & Radcliffe, E. 2007. *Colorado Potato Beetle.* Dept. Of Entomology, University of Minnesota. www.vegedge.umn.edu/vegpest/cpb.htm.

Robinson, Raoul A. *Amateur Potato Breeders Manual.* Free download from www.sharebooks.ca.

Salaman, Redcliffe N. 1970. *The History and Social Influence of the Potato,* Cambridge University Press.

Seaman, A., Tingey, W., Power, A., Halseth, D., De Jong, W. *Potato Varietal Mixtures for Potato Leafhopper Management on Organic Farms.* Cornell University. www.nysipm.cornell.edu/grantspgm/projects/proj06/veg/seaman3.asp

The descriptions of potato varieties were obtained from the following sources:

OMAFRA. *Vegetable Production Recommendations* 2006–2007. Ontario Ministry of Agriculture, Food and Rural Affairs, Publication no. 363, www.omafra.gov.on.ca/english/products/hort.html

British Columbia Vegetable Production Guide www.al.gov.bc.ca/fieldvegetable/production_guide/2008_2009/production_guide.htm

British Potato Variety Database varieties.potato.org.uk

CFIA potato variety registration www.inspection.gc.ca

European Union Potato Database www.europotato.org/display_description.php

4 Soil fertility on the organic potato farm

Brown, Christine. 2007. Available Nutrients & Value for Manure from Various Livestock Types. *Nutrient Management Field Crops.* Ontario Ministry of Agriculture, Food & Rural Affairs (OMAFRA).

Coleman, Eliot. 1995. *The New Organic Grower.* Old Bridge Press.

Kinsey, Neal & Walters, Charles. 2006. *Hands-On Agronomy.* Acres U.S.A.

Lynch, D. From a conversation with Dr. Derek Lynch of the Organic Agriculture Centre of Canada about the research by one of his graduate students, E. Clegg.

Nelson, K., Lynch, D., and Boiteau, G. *Soil Health in Organic Potato Systems.* Organic Agriculture Centre, Technical Bulletin E2008–22 www.organicagcentre.ca/Docs/TechnicalBulletins08/TechnicalBulletin22web_potato.pdf

OMAFRA. 2008. *Field Crop Budgets.* Publication no. 060. http://www.omafra.gov.on.ca/english/busdev/facts/pub60.htm

OMAFRA 1997. *Soil Management: Best Management Practices* www.omafra.gov.on.ca/english/environment/bmp/series.htm

OMAFRA. *Vegetable Production Recommendations* 2006–2007. Ontario Ministry of Agriculture, Food and Rural Affairs, Publication no. 363, www.omafra.gov.on.ca/english/products/hort.html

PEI Ministry of Agriculture. 2000. *Agricultural Business Profile on Organic Potatoes.* www.gov.pe.ca/af/agweb/index.php3?number=atoz

Sayre, Laura. 2003. *Cultivating Diversity Underground for Better Yields Above.* Available online at www.rodaleinstitute.org/new_farm

Tugel, Arlene, Ann Lewandowski, Deb Happe-vonArb, eds. 2000. *Soil Biology Primer.* Iowa: Soil and Water Conservation Society.

Soil Biology Primer, USDA NRCS Publication, 2000

Rodale, The New Farm Fact Sheet, 2003. *My-Core-What? The blow-by-blow on beneficial root fungi, mycorrhizas – rocket boosters for your plants.* www.rodaleinstitute.org

Sustainable Agriculture Network. 2007. *Managing Cover Crops Profitably,* Handbook Series Book 9. www.sare.org/publications/index.htm

Wallace, Janet, ed. 2001. *Organic Field Crop Handbook.* Canadian Organic Growers.

Walters, Charles & Fenzau, C.J. 1996. *Eco-Farm: An Acres U.S.A. Primer.* Acres U.S.A.

5 Organic seed potato production

Alberta Ministry of Agriculture & Food. *Seed Potato Production Guide.* www1.agric.gov.ab.ca/$department/deptdocs.nsf/all/opp9641

Canadian Food Inspection Agency (CFIA) Application forms for new seed growers are available from the Canadian Food Inspection Agency. The deadline for applications is June 15th of the crop year. The contact information for CFIA can be found on their website: www.inspection.gc.ca

Manitoba Agriculture, Food & Rural Initiatives. *Potato Production – Seed Potato Production Management.* www.gov.mb.ca/agriculture/crops/potatoes/bda04s11.html

---

6 Planting & cultivation

www.cmn.dk/indexuk.htm (Couch Grass Killer machinery)

Duval, Jean. Controlling Quackgrass. *The Canadian Organic Grower,* Summer 2006.

Ivany, Jerry A. 2002. Physical Weed Control in Potatoes. 5th EWRS Workshop on Physical Weed Control, Pisa Italy.

Factsheets on Potato Production. PEI Ministry of Agriculture. www.gov.pe.ca/af/agweb/index.php3?number=70748&lang=E

Kinsey, N. & Walters, C. 2006. *Hands-On Agronomy.* Acres USA

Pfeiffer, Ehrenfried E. 1970. *Weeds and What They Tell.* Biodynamic Farming & Gardening Association.

Physiological Age and Seed Preparation. New Brunswick Agriculture, Fisheries and Aquaculture, www.gnb.ca/0029/00290002-e.asp

Swanton, Clarence. Integrated Weed Management Strategies for Organic Farmers. Presentation at Guelph Organic Conference, January 2008.

---

7 Disease & pest prevention

Altieri, Miguel A.et al. 2005. *Manage Insects on your Farm: A Guide to Ecological Strategies.* Sustainable Agriculture Network

See also Chapter 8 & 9 Resources.

8 The challenge: pests

ACORN Directory of Allowable Organic Inputs (ACORN) is available online at www.acornorganic.org/acorn/index.html

Altieri, M.A. & Nicholls, C.I. 2005. *Managing Insects on Your Farm: A Guide to Ecological Strategies.* Sustainable Agriculture Network.

Bartsova, Dr. & Rifai, Dr. Nabil. 1999. *Bio-collector as an Alternative Method for the Control of the Colorado potato beetle in Organic Farming.* Nova Scotia Agriculture College.

Bernard, Guy. *Organic Potato Production – A Pest Management Perspective Part One: Insect Control.* Organic Agricultural Centre of Canada. www.organicagcentre.ca/NewspaperArticles/na_org_pot_part1.asp

Boiteau, G., Lynch D.H. & Martin, R.C. 2008. Influence of Fertilization on the Colorado potato beetle, Leptinotarsa decemlineata in organic potato production. *Journal of Environmental Entomology,* 37(2).

Caldwell, Brian. 2004. *Starflower and Freeville Organic Potato Trials.* Cornell University. Available online at www.plbr.cornell.edu/PSI/StarflowerandFreevillePotato04.pdf

CFIA. *Quarantine notifications.*
www.inspection.gc.ca/english/plaveg/pestrava/gloros/glorose.shtml

Cornell University. *Integrated Crop and Pest Management Guidelines: Potatoes.* Cornell University Extension: www.nysaes.cornell.edu/recommends/24frameset.html

Ellis, B.W. & Bradley, F.M., eds. 1992. *The Organic Gardener's Handbook of Natural Insect and Disease Control.* Rodale Press.

Everts, Kathryne L. et al. *Cover Crops Deter Root-Damaging Nematodes in Vegetable Systems.* Conference 2003 Highlights, Sustainable Agriculture Research and Education. www.sare.org/highlights/2003/nematode.htm

Frost David et al. 2002. *Wireworm Control Using Fodder Rape and Mustard – Evaluating the Use of Brassica Green Manures for the Control of Wireworms in Organic Crops.* ADAS. Available at www.orgprints.org

Hiiesaar, K. et al. 2006. Over-wintering of the Colorado potato beetle (*Leptinotarsa decemlineata Say*) in field conditions and factors affecting its population density in Estonia. *Agronomy Research* 4(1).

Lampkin, Nicholas. 2002. *Organic Farming.* Old Pond.

Loo, R. et al. *An Evaluation of a Number of Potato Varieties as Insect Catch Crops: On-Farm Organic Trial.* Available online at www.organicagcentre.ca

Mans, Hida. 2007. *An Organic Equilibrium Through Mulching.* Guelph Organic Agricultural Conference. Proceedings available at www.guelphorganicconf.ca

Marshall, Stephen A. 2006. *Insects: Their Natural History and Diversity.* Firefly Books.

Neel, Caroline S. 1992. *Alternative Methods for Controlling the Colorado potato beetle.* West Virginia University Centre for Sustainable and Alternative Agriculture. www.wvu.edu/~exten/infores/pubs/pest/altmeth.pdf

OMAFRA. *Vegetable Production Recommendations* 2008–2009, Ontario Ministry of Agriculture, Food & Rural Affairs, Publication No.363

Panhwar, Farzana. 2004. Controlling pests with plants. *Eco-Farm & Garden,* Spring 2004. Canadian Organic Growers.

Rodale Institute's organic experimental farm publishes information online at: www.rodaleinstitute.org. The website offers practical advice on pest control strategies as well as farm profiles.

SARE 2003 Highlights. 2003. *Cover Crops Deter Root-Damaging Nematodes in Vegetable Systems.* SARE LNE00-131. Available online at www.sare.org/projects

Salaman, Redcliffe N. 1970. *The History and Social Influence of the Potato.* Cambridge University Press.

Sayre, Laura. 2005. *Banking on BARC (Mulching potatoes).* The New Farm, Rodale Institute. www.newfarm.org

Seaman, Abby. *Potato Leafhopper.* Cornell University IPM Extension Factsheet. nysipm.cornell.edu/vegetables/nofa/default.asp

Stoner, Kimberly A. 1998, *Alternatives to Insecticides for Managing Vegetable Insects.* (Proceedings of a Farmer/Scientist Conference) Natural Resource, Agriculture, and Engineering Service (NRAES-138). www.nraes.org

Wheeler, Robin. February, 2004. The Worrisome Lowdown on the Wiley Wireworm. *BC Organic Grower.* www.certifiedorganic.bc.ca

Sources of Beneficial Insects: Ordering information is available online at
- www.thebugfactory.ca (Spined Soldier Bugs)
- www.biobest.be (Parasitic Wasps)
- www.naturalinsectocontrol.ca (Ladybugs, Nematodes)
- www.insectary.com
- www.nematodary.com
- www.benemite.com
- www.ipmlabs.com
- www.sterlingnursery.com
- www.biologicco.com

9 The challenge: diseases

Appropriate Technology Transfer Agency (ATTRA) is a program of the United States Department of Agriculture and is an excellent resource for research on organic production methods: www.attra.org.

Banks, Dr. Eugenia. 2004. *Potato Field Guide: Insects, Diseases and Defects.* OMAFRA publication no. 823

Burrows, Mary E. & Zitter Thomas A. 2005. *Virus Problems of Potatoes.* USDA-ARS & Dept. of Plant Pathology, Cornell University.

Canadian Food Inspection Agency: Information on virus quarantine outbreaks in Canada is available online at www.inspection.gc.ca

Doring, Thomas & Sauke, Helmut. 2003. *Straw Mulch and Chitting for Virus Vector Control in Organic Potatoes.* Organic E-prints. www.orgprints.org

Ellis, Barbara W. & Fern, Marshall Bradley, eds. 1992. The *Organic Gardener's Handbook of Natural Insect and Disease Control.* Rodale Press.

Forrer, H.R. et al. 2006. Control of *Phytophthera infestans* in organic potato production, Organic E-prints. www.orgprints.org

Ingham, Elaine. 2005. *The Compost Tea Brewing Manual: Latest Methods and Research.* Soil Food Web Inc.

Kuepper, George & Sullivan, Preston. 2004. *Organic Alternatives for Late Blight Control in Potatoes.* ATTRA. www.attra.org

Leifert, Dr. Carlo. 2004. *Novel Strategies for Control of Fungal Crop Disease.* OACC Potato Symposium. www.organicagcentre.ca/Potato%20Symposium/index.html

Marshall, Stephen A. 2006. *Insects: Their Natural History & Diversity.* Firefly Books.

Merida, C.L. & Loria, R. 1991. *Silver Scurf of Potato.* Cooperative Extension Fact Sheet Page: 725.90 Cornell University, Dept. of Plant Pathology.

Peters, Rick. 2004. *Seafood Processing Waste for Nutrition & Disease Control in Organically Grown Potatoes.* OACC Potato Symposium. www.organicagcentre.ca/Potato%20Symposium/index.html

Sayre, Laura. 2003. *Compost Tea Research Enters Its 2nd Year.* Rodale Institute. www.newfarm.org

Shinners-Carnelley, Tracy et al. *Commercial Potato Production & Disease Management.* Manitoba Agriculture, Food & Rural Initiatives. www.gov.mb.ca/agriculture/crops/potatoes/bda04s07(3-4).htmlno. Bacterial_Diseases

Sideman, Eric et al. 2004. *Compost Tea Task Force Report.* National Organic Standards Board. www.ams.usda.gov/AMSv1.0/getfile?dDocName=STELPRDC5058470

Stoner, Kimberly A. 1998. *Alternatives to Insecticides for Managing Vegetable Insects.* (Proceedings of a Farmer/Scientist Conference) Natural Resource, Agriculture, and Engineering Service (NRAES-138). www.nraes.org

Sturz, A.V. et al. 2006. Influence of compost tea, powdered kelp and Manzate 75 on bacterial-community composition, and antibiosis against *Phytophthora infestans* in the potato phylloplane. *Canadian Journal of Plant Pathology.* 28

Viruses, Viroids and Mycoplasmas. Prince Edward Island Ministry of Agriculture Factsheet. www.gov.pe.ca/af/agweb/index.php3?number=1001566

Zitter, Thomas A. & Loria, Rosemary. *Detection of Potato Tuber Diseases & Defects.* Cooperative Extension Information Bulletin 205. Cornell University, Dept. of Plant Pathology.

10 Harvesting & storage

Atlantic Potato Committee. *Atlantic Canada Potato Guide.* www.gov.pe.ca/af/agweb/

Elsadr, H. & Waterer, D. 2005. *Efficacy of Natural Compounds to Suppress Sprouting and Fusarium Dry Rot in Potatoes.* University of Saskatchewan. www.usask.ca/agriculture/plantssci/vegetable

Harvy, Roger. 1995. *Potato Compost: Production & Use.* P.E.I. Department of Agriculture, Agdex no. 530. www.gov.pe.ca/af/agweb/

Snowden, Murray. *Feeding Potatoes to Cattle.* New Brunswick Department of Agriculture. www.gnb.ca/0170/01700002-e/asp

United Kingdom Soil Association. *Organic Potato Production & Storage.* Soil Association Technical Guides for Organic Crop & Livestock Production.

Weston, J.W. 1922. *Feeding Cull and Surplus Potatoes.* Michigan Agriculture College. web1.msue.msu.edu/imp/modp1/morefile/E0025.pdf

11 Marketing organic potatoes

Delanoy, L. et al. 2003. *Organic and Pesticide Free Potato Production.* Saskatchewan Ministry of Agriculture. www.agriculture.gov.sk.ca

Macey, Anne. 2008. *Certified Organic Production in Canada.* Canadian Organic Growers. (annual statistics available at www.cog.ca)

MacRae, Rod et al. 2006. *Ontario Goes Organic: How to Access Canada's Growing Billion Dollar Market For Organic Food.* World Wildlife Fund Canada & Organic Agriculture Centre of Canada. www.organicagcentre.ca/ResearchDatabase/res_oos_intro.asp

Pawlick, Thomas F. 2006. *The End Of Food: How The Food Industry Is Destroying Our Food Supply – And What You Can Do About It.* Greystone Books.

Glossary

Allelopathy
The release of a chemical by plants which prevents the germination of other (weed) seeds.

Beneficial Insect
A species of insect which serves a useful function on the farm, such as pollinating crops or eating pest insects.

Blind Harrowing
Taking a harrow across a crop that has been seeded, but has not yet emerged (also called pre-emergence tillage).

Buffer (buffering agent)
An alkaline substance which is fed to reduce the acidity of livestock feed.

Catch Crop
A cover crop planted to take up excess nutrients, reducing nutrient leaching. Nutrients are released when the catch crop is turned under.

Chitting
The practice of pre-sprouting seed potatoes to hasten growth.

Conventional agriculture
'Conventional' is used to describe non-organic farming methods.

Cull potatoes
Potatoes which are green, diseased or bruised, and disposed of by composting, burial or use as animal feed.

Cultivation
The practice of mechanically breaking up soil around growing crops to uproot weeds.

Dormancy
The potato tubers' state of inactivity from harvest until spring.

Foliar Spray (Feeds)
Liquid amendments which are sprayed on the leaf surface and absorbed directly into the cells.

Fresh Chipping Potatoes
Varieties of potatoes (such as Atlantic and Cascade) which are harvested out of the field and shipped immediately for processing into potato chips.

Green Manure
A crop which covers the soil and reduces soil erosion, as well as fixes nitrogen and improves tilth (also called cover crops, plowdowns or catch crops).

Green Sprouting
See Chitting.

Greenstone
A paramagnetic rock dust. An iron-rich seabed volcanic deposit which combines metasedimentary and metavolcanic rock with high levels of silicates. Greenstone also contains 4% potassium, 1% calcium, 1% magnesium, 10% iron, 7% aluminum with trace levels of phosphorus, sodium and titanium.

Humus
The stable portion of soil organic matter resulting from the decomposition of plant, animal and microbial tissues.

Hundred Weight
CWT is an American unit of weight equivalent to one hundred pounds and is called a hundredweight. It is used by many potato producers to calculate yields.

Inert
Substances such as surfactants which are added to commercial formulations to improve the product's efficacy.

Inoculant
Commercial preparation of the spores of nitrogen-fixing Rhizobia which is applied to legume seed when planted; OR, any material of high microbial activity (e.g. mycorrhizal fungi) added to the soil at planting to stimulate biological activity.

Input
See soil amendment.

Insectary strip
Bed located within a field, planted to flowering plants which attract and support beneficial insects.

Legume
A member of the plant family, *Leguminosae,* which includes clover, alfalfa, beans, peas and sweet clover. The roots of legumes host nitrogen-fixing bacteria (Rhizobia) in a symbiotic relationship.

Mycorrhizal association
A symbiotic relationship between mycorrhizal fungi and plant roots, in which soil nutrients such as phosphorus are made into a form that plants can take up more easily.

Niche market
Market that develops as a result of changing tastes or cultural preferences.

Nitrogen-fixation
The conversion of nitrogen gas to a form of nitrogen useable by plant roots; this is accomplished by Rhizobia bacteria living in the nodules of legumes.

Organic matter
An important part of the soil consisting of the living bodies, remains and waste products of living organisms.

pH
The concentration of hydrogen ions in a solution that demonstrates the acidity or alkalinity of the solution. A pH of 7 is neutral; lower numbers indicate acidic conditions; higher numbers indicate alkaline conditions.

Paramagnetism
The theory that magnetism in amendments contributes to the movement of nutrients in the soil food web.

Plowdown
The incorporation of a green manure crop into the soil by plowing or disking.

Resistance
The genetic predisposition to remain healthy after being exposed to a pathogen. Also refers to the state of health of the plant and its ability to resist infection, even if a specific genetic trait is not present.

Rhizobia
Nitrogen-fixing bacteria that live symbiotically in the roots of legumes.

Rogue, rogue out
To hand pick weeds, volunteers or diseased plants while scouting fields.

Scouting
Inspecting the field for pests, diseased plants, or weeds.

Soil amendment
Any material added to the soil to enhance soil biological activity.

Soil organisms
Creatures such as earthworms, ground beetles, centipedes, bacteria, protozoa and fungi that inhabit the soil and, among other activities, convert nutrients to a form plants can utilize.

Spinosad
Spinosad is an aerobic fermentation product of *Saccharopolyspora spinosa*, a soil bacteria, which is used by organic farmers as a pesticide.

Suberization
The process by which surface tissues of the potato tuber heal.

Sustainability
The principle of utilizing resources in a way which does not deplete them.

Thermophilic Phase
The heating phase in composting (up to 55°C/131 °F) which destroys pathogenic microorganisms and weed seeds.

Tillage
The mechanical disturbance of the soil to prepare the seedbed, control weeds, incorporate soil amendments and, by loosening soil, incorporate oxygen.

Tiller
A form of plant reproduction by the growth of stolons which send up more shoots resulting in greater coverage of the soil and better competition with the weeds.

Tilth
The physical quality or condition of soil.

Top-kill
The destruction of the vines to initiate hardening of the skins in preparation for harvest.

Trap Crop
A crop which is planted for the purpose of attracting pest insects away from the main crop.

Volunteers
Plants that grow from potatoes which have survived freezing temperatures.